HOW TO MAKE PEOPLE LIKE YOU

Books by Lelord Kordel

HEALTH THROUGH NUTRITION

EAT AND GROW YOUNGER

LADY, BE LOVED!

EAT YOUR TROUBLES AWAY

LIVE TO ENJOY THE MONEY YOU MAKE

HOW TO MAKE PEOPLE LIKE YOU

LELORD KORDEL

How To Make People Like You

THE WORLD PUBLISHING COMPANY

CLEVELAND AND NEW YORK

Published by The World Publishing Company

2231 West 110th Street, Cleveland 2, Ohio

Published simultaneously in Canada by

Nelson, Foster & Scott Ltd.

Library of Congress Catalog Card Number: 59-7747

FIRST EDITION

For their unselfish and significant individual contributions toward a better, broader understanding of the importance of nutrition to improved health and longer life . . . the author, with deep respect, dedicates this volume to:

DR. C. WARD CRAMPTON

DR. CHARLES RICHET

J. I. RODALE

Each one, in his own special way, has done much to help mankind.

Contents

CONTENTS

HOW TO MAKE PEOPLE LIKE YOU

Your Personality and You

YOUR personality is *you!*
The whole you—fashioned from the blueprints of your heredity . . . your mother's during pregnancy . . . and the past and present nourishment of your own body. It is the sum total of what you are—or can be. It can create happiness and success for you . . . or it can be the cause of untold misery, frustration, and defeat.

What about *your* personality?

Do you get along well with others, co-operate readily, and make friends quickly? Or do you lose jobs frequently, even though you are an experienced and competent worker? Has the harmony in your home decreased to an alarming extent, in spite of the fact that you really love your family?

Then look to your personality!

It's the major factor in loss of jobs and marriage failures.

Personality factors are considered by business leaders at between 85 and 90 per cent of your total rating. Studies at Purdue and other leading universities have found that the students with the highest personality ratings in college later achieved the greatest success in their professions.

"All right," you may say. "I know all this is true. I've seen men with half my ability get ahead, while I plod along year after year without making a bit of progress. But you either have personality or you haven't, and there's nothing you can do about it."

Isn't there?

The Chinese have a saying that a journey of a thousand miles starts with but a single step.

Will you take that first step with me, and let the rest of the way unfold as we go along? I promise you that the results will astonish you!

But first, let's go back a few years to your beginning. You began with just one cell in your mother's womb, and were nourished to become a many-trillion-cell infant. These cells range from the simple skin cells that are constantly growing and being rubbed off to the complex network of nerve cells and fibers that is the brain.

And in your mother's womb, your personality was first influenced. Scientific tests have proved that well-nourished mothers (especially those whose diets were high in vitamins and minerals during pregnancy) produce more intelligent babies.

Through the nutrition of your mother, you received a heritage of health which built your personality, cell by cell. Your height and weight vary directly with the amount of protein that your mother consumed before your birth and that you received during childhood.

It isn't just coincidence that today's children are taller and sturdier than the last generation. The youngsters who are stronger, brighter, and more alert than their playmates are invariably those who have been vitamin-fed since infancy.

Unfortunately, there are still too many American children who have less than optimum muscle development, because of inadequate protein intake. A daily consumption of less than 75 grams of protein by the mother during the latter part of pregnancy results in an infant who will tend to be short, light in weight, and likely to receive a low pediatric rating in other respects.

Doctors H. D. Lynch and W. D. Snively report that protein

deficiency is "one of the most prevalent clinically manifested deficiency diseases which affects children."

They list anorexia (poor appetite), irritability, vomiting, poor muscular development, constipation, increased susceptibility to infections, a high rate of dental cavities, and anemia as the common symptoms of protein deficiency.

The personality cannot develop without adequate nutrients.

"Are you trying to tell me," you ask, "that my personality, or lack of it, depends on what I eat?"

Exactly!

Your personality depends upon your physical health. Illness and low physical stamina account for most of the defeated personalities, the majority of life's failures. Look around you at the successful men and women. They generally have at least two outstanding attributes in common: vitality and enthusiasm.

"I *used* to have a lot of enthusiasm," you tell me, "and plenty of vitality, too. But that was when I was younger. Now I'm tired. When I get through work I just don't have any energy left. I feel dull, mentally and physically, and realize that I wouldn't be good company for anybody if I did try to go out for a social evening. So I just sit home and become more discouraged and depressed. What's wrong with me, anyway?"

"What's wrong with me?"

That's the question I am asked almost daily by people coming to my office for help. Many of these persons are suffering from deficiency diseases. Some of them are nervous, neurotic, and in a state of mind that makes them afraid to face the world.

All of them have personalities.

But they are defeated personalities, in whom illness, chronic fatigue, and lack of stamina caused by poor nutrition have created maladjustments and fostered neurotic tendencies.

During the four important periods of infancy, adolescence, involution, and early senescence, your personality is most liable to succumb to the stresses of life. The failure of the endocrine glands during involution contributes to the involutional psychoses that make up between 5 and 10 per cent of mental hospital admissions.

Poor sex development—even poor breast development, which can give a woman an inferiority complex in this day and age when glamour is measured by vital statistics!—is often due to anemia or a lack in nutrition during adolescence.

As you grow older, the nutritional deficiencies compound into a poor condition of both body and mind. The some ten million living wires, or nerve fibers, which keep the flow of electrical impulses in a constant two-way traffic between the two parts of the brain are affected by the chemical deficiencies caused by inadequate diets. This results in schizophrenia and other mental diseases.

About 50 per cent of the adult patients who visit general practitioners are suffering from symptoms associated with mental illness or personality disturbances.

Nearly 30 per cent of all patients who go to general hospitals have psychiatric problems.

The degenerative disorders of hypertension and diseases of the coronary arteries are the result of stresses created in both the mind and the body. High-fat diets clog the bloodstream with cholesterol; the flow of blood is retarded, or even stopped in coronary thrombosis.

These diseases may represent as well the final results of years of tension in persons whose personalities and social defenses are sufficiently strong to resist the development of an overt neurosis. The hypertensive and the coronary personalities are so prevalent that I shall discuss them at length in later chapters.

Far too many persons suffer, both mentally and physically, from a high-carbohydrate diet. Carbohydrates are so high in calories that they prevent the ingestion of other foods essential to control disease and produce health benefits.

If you by-pass meat, fresh fruit, and vegetables and load your plate with macaroni, spaghetti, hot breads, and rich pastries, it goes without saying that you are (or will become!) overweight. You will develop nutritional disturbances which will impair your personality and inhibit both your work and your play by the resulting listlessness, neurasthenia, heart consciousness, gas eructations, edema, and other ailments.

Perhaps too late you find that your high-carbohydrate diet has caused impairment in specific physiologic systems, of which the gonads have been the hardest hit, and you are suffering from the disease of aging.

Personality may be compared to a small stream in its continuous flow through life. And like life, your stream is in a constant state of flux, changing, twisting, and swelling with every foot of ground that it covers and with every day that it exists. Your personality becomes your individual mode of striving to meet your needs and to manage the demands of your social reality.

Your needs are forged by your style of life. Yet your personality can forge a new style of life for you.

It is in your power to prevent or overcome much illness, tear down the prison walls of fixity, fear, and anxiety, and swell this tiny, choked stream into a river of success and achievement.

Many factors of human development and behavior make up your personality. According to Gordon Allport, the famous sociologist, your personality is an organization of psychophysical systems that influence specific acts.

Physically, the blueprints of your heredity produced you out of simple groceries.

If they were the raw materials for growth and development (proteins, vitamins, and minerals!), and if the determinants were in the proper pattern, then your personality becomes the efficient chemical machine that will enable you to reach the potential of your talents.

Unfortunately, however, all personalities do not inherit perfect patterns. Diabetics have perhaps inherited a lacking in the specialized cells of the islands of Langerhans, where insulin is secreted that controls the amount of sugar in the blood. The anemic may have inherited the inability to metabolize iron. Recent tests show that the alcoholic has probably inherited the inability to extract sufficient vitamin B from the food he eats.

Each personality has its hereditary disposition to strength or weakness. These chemical and preneurotic tendencies determine your ability to stand up to the inevitable crises of life.

Dr. W. Horsley Gantt, of Johns Hopkins University, is convinced that if these hereditary dispositions to strength or weakness under stress can be discovered in time, *then the personality can take fundamental precautions against mental or physical breakdowns.*

The cases of powerful personalities that have developed and talents (or genius!) that have emerged out of seemingly hopeless handicaps are almost too well known to bear repeating, except as reminders of what can be done. Helen Keller, deaf and blind since infancy . . . Charles Steinmetz, the dwarfed and crippled electrical genius . . . Byron with his clubfoot—the list is endless.

Although the breakdown of the personality is, in some cases, due to inherited chemical deficiencies, inadequate nutrition is the more prevalent cause of such a breakdown.

The personality is not a fixed entity. It may also be influenced by the environment in which it grows.

Queen Elizabeth II of England inherited a tendency to plumpness from her mother. As a princess, she became overweight by eating the rich foods served to her in the palace. After she fell in love with Prince Philip, she began to diet, and by the time she ascended the throne she had become the lovely, slender queen that she is today.

Dieting has now become such a habit that she no longer craves fattening foods. She eats no sauces or gravies, any nibble between meals is confined to fruit, and at banquets the queen eats fish or fruit for her first course, a main course of meat and vegetables, and a simple dessert of fruit and cheese.

After the queen eliminated carbohydrates from her diet, her personality began to emerge, more stimulating and brilliant than it had ever been.

A well-balanced diet is the best and cheapest type of health insurance that you can buy. And the best thing to save for your old age is your health.

How mature and well-adjusted is *your* personality? Do you have the ability to make and carry out intelligent plans for your future? Do you have a unifying philosophy of life, and the habit of living by principles instead of by emotionalized decisions of the moment?

Are you able to take responsibility, survey your abilities and limitations, and make the most of them?

Can you accomplish what you set out to do, laugh at your mistakes, and see yourself as others see you?

When you can answer these questions in the affirmative, when you can watch the breaking of the things to which you gave your life and can stoop and rebuild them with worn-out tools, then, as Kipling said, "You'll be a man, my son!"

The personality that is confident, that believes he is strong, has a muscular output much greater than that of the man who feels whipped. The defeated personality slumps in fatigue, feels that his strength is limited, and becomes discouraged and further fatigued.

He may be a breakfast-skipper, who robs himself of potential alertness and efficiency during the late morning hours. He is quite likely a victim of the insidious high-carbohydrate diet.

No manufacturer of high-calorie foods ever tells his overweight customers, "Eat less of my product!" Yet by consuming as many as 200,000 excess calories during your lifetime, you will reduce your life expectancy about five years.

The defeated personality advertises his failure to the world in his posture, his walk, the tone of his voice, and his mannerisms. He freezes his reservoir of freely mobile energy, either with the chronic fatigue of a diet inadequate in proteins, vitamins, and minerals or by the fears and anxieties compounded by his physical inadequacies.

He doesn't eat enough muscle-building protein to enable him to straighten his shoulders, hold his head high, raise his chest and breathe deeply. He can't step out with a firm and confident stride, because his blood sugar is too low. His voice becomes old and tired, and his starved nerves cause mannerisms that are fussy, nervous, and the product of uncontrolled tensions.

Sexual vigor is one of the first losses of the defeated personality. When the general health is impaired and the vital energies are low, the sexual organs are weakened, and usually proportionately more than any other.

Starvation of the tissue-building foods is felt in his liver, his heart, and his kidneys. His glands fail to function properly. He contributes to the breakdown of these organs with a daily bombardment of empty calories of fats, sugars, and starches. If he lives beyond his middle years, his nutritional deficiencies may cause senility of the brain, arteriosclerosis, and demineralization of his bones.

"All right," I hope you're saying by now, "you've convinced me. And I don't want to be like this defeated personality you've been describing."

You don't have to be! No doubt, you've always intended some day to start eating the foods that will build a stronger body and a more positive personality. Some day. But when?

What's wrong with now?

Start this important journey one step at a time, learning and growing with each successive step, and you'll find your progress easy. Don't expect to arrive by jet propulsion. It isn't that fast, but it's steady and sure, and you'll gain the healthy and wholesome use of your resources for happy, confident living.

The starting point is a place called Beginning Again.

Will you come with me and discover your own personality type and its specific nutritional needs?

In that discovery lies the secret of how to make people like you!

2

Personality Types:
Which One Are You?

WE SAT, relaxed and comfortable, Will Nelson and I, under the shade of an oak tree on the spacious Nelson lawn. A breeze rustled the leaves in the treetop and swayed the white linen on the tables that dotted the lawn.

It was the Nelsons' annual family reunion, and Will had especially asked me to attend. Life seemed serene and peaceful here, although I knew that right now the kitchen was the scene of bustling activity, and that children were playing noisily in various parts of the house and grounds.

Fresh strawberries, raspberries, peaches, grapes, and black cherries were already on the table, along with iced melons and fruit juices. As we sat and talked, Will and I were served honeydew with fresh lime. But Will's brother, Dave, would have none of these vitamin-mineral-packed delicacies.

"I've got to have more substantial food than that," he said, "to give me energy. If I don't eat a lot, I'm tired all the time."

Now, just control yourself, Kordel, I thought. You're enjoying the Nelsons' hospitality, so don't say anything. And don't give them a lecture on proteins, vitamins, and minerals when it isn't asked for or wanted.

Will Nelson looked at his brother with mild distaste. "But, Dave," he said, "these melons and fruits are just starters. You know very well that you'll have all the substantial food you can eat later on. Better save room for it."

"Plenty of room here." Dave laughed, patting his plump, sagging belly, and wandered off toward the kitchen.

"I've been trying to get Dave to come see you," Will said. "I'm worried about him. You know he's sales manager of our business, and has always done a terrific job until lately. Now he's slipping pretty badly, both mentally and physically, and it's showing up in many ways—in his personality, which used to be such an asset in selling, in his health and his appearance. He says all he needs is lots of good, hearty food to give him energy, and that's what you advocate."

I watched Dave as he reappeared with a loaded plate of macaroni and cheese, fried potatoes, hot rolls, and a big wedge of layer cake with thick chocolate frosting. "This is *my* first course," he said, wolfing it down as he passed us, headed toward the hammock.

"It's easy to see," I said, "that Dave's definition of *good, hearty food* is not the same as mine. The trick is to make him see it. This is certainly a case in which a *little* knowledge is a dangerous thing. And I *do* mean dangerous, literally."

"I'd appreciate anything you can do for him," Will said. "He complains of being tired all the time, he's lost his jolly disposition and his memory has gotten so bad that you'd think he was an old man, yet he's four years younger than I am. I don't know what it is, but something's sure happened to him."

Something had, indeed, happened to Dave. I looked across the yard to the hammock where he was lying, his empty plate beside him on the grass. He was dozing now, with his hands folded across his pudgy stomach, and his breathing was heavy and labored. His face was pale, and it wasn't the afternoon sunlight that gave it a yellowish cast.

You might assume that the similarity of hereditary genes would produce similar people. The Nelsons all had a marked family resemblance, but that was as far as it went. They differed in body build and personality—some were quick-tempered and some placid, a few were lazy and others were ambitious. This is true of most families.

When Will and Dave were in grammar school, they had resembled each other almost enough to be twins. Today I could see not a particle of resemblance between the two brothers, except in the color of the eyes. Yet while they possessed the same shade of brown, Dave's eyes had become red-rimmed, lusterless, and tired-looking. He lacked the clear direct gaze, the vitality and animation that his brother's eyes retained.

Exhausted or not, Dave managed to rise from his hammock when he heard the rattle of dishes and realized that food was being put on the tables. Will and I looked over the huge platters of roast beef, fried chicken, baked ham, creamed dishes, hot breads, vegetables, salads, and homemade cakes and pies. Then each of us settled for roast beef, salad, and green vegetables.

But not Dave! Once more he loaded his plate with the fattest, starchiest food in sight, including two kinds of potatoes and both hot rolls and biscuits. Between bites, he looked at Will and me rather enviously, and said, "I don't see how you fellows keep your figures."

"I can see why you don't," I couldn't help answering.

That put him on the defensive, and he said, "I have to eat like this, or I don't have a bit of pep. I'm just all worn out. And you know you always say that you have to eat to restore your energy."

"Yes," I said, "I always do say that. But at the same time I specify the *kind* of food to eat—foods rich in proteins, vitamins, and minerals. Certainly not the high-carbohydrate foods that you've been stowing away all day. No human being can eat like that without causing almost irreparable damage to both his body and personality. And you, with your particular body build and the tendency to put on weight, should be doubly protein-vitamin-and-mineral-conscious."

Dave paused over his second dessert to ask, "What's my body build got to do with it?"

"You belong to the viscerotonia classification," I told him, "the type in which the function of the digestive organs predominates."

To a great extent, your personality is determined by the most dominating attributes of your body. Dr. William Sheldon categorized the attributes that are largely responsible for your physical personality before you are born. Your personality may be influenced by your digestive organs, by your muscles, or by your brain. All of these have some influence upon your physical personality, but one of them exerts a much stronger influence upon you than the other two.

Under normal growing and living conditions, your dominant body function will contribute enough to your appearance to type you physically. There are some instances (where the mental or the emotional personality does not dominate the physical personality) in which your body type can often give advance clues to your personality traits.

According to Dr. Sheldon's *viscerotonia* classification, the group in whom the function of the digestive organs predominates are easygoing, relaxed, comfort-loving people. They enjoy eating, are good-natured, gregarious, tolerant, extroverted, and talkative.

The viscerotonia personality craves companionship and needs strong family relationships. They sleep easily and deeply. In appearance they are likely to be soft and fat, with a roundness and fullness of body. This type has an intestinal tract that is muscularly sluggish and retains food until every morsel is digested and absorbed. Such a complete utilization of food tends to make them gain weight easily.

When you hear a person complain, "Everything I eat turns to fat!" you may be sure that it's the viscerotonia personality speaking.

If you are this type, you have a good cushion of fat about the great nerve ganglia in the abdomen, which tends to keep you from becoming nervous, irritable, or unduly sensitive. This, along with your excellent digestion, possibly accounts for your placid disposition. You should eat plenty of the low-calorie, bulky, fibrous fruits and vegetables for that sluggish intestinal tract, the proteins of lean meat, poultry, fish, eggs, powdered skim milk, and cottage cheese to normalize your weight and prevent hunger pangs . . . *and from this moment on,* eliminate fats, sugars, and starches from your diet.

Another body type is found in the *somatotonia* group, which is primarily oriented by the muscular structure of the body. Their marked characteristics are high energy, the love of physical adventure, enjoyment of life, need of exercise, leadership and domination of others, boldness and a gambling spirit. They are generally energetic, frank, and responsible, but, on the negative side, they may also be insensitive, overaggressive, ruthless, and brutal.

This personality type matures early and shows an overmaturity in his appearance. You recognize him in a crowd by his large, rectangular-shaped body and broad shoulders. He often has lean, trim hips and powerful legs. He needs protein in abundance to keep his muscles firm and strong and for energy. He is so active physically that he may consume more calories than the viscerotonia personality, without the tendency to become overweight.

If you are this type, the aggressive, competitive go-getter, you will live under such stress that you may well become a victim of high blood pressure and heart disease. As a precaution, eliminate all fats from your diet, have your steaks broiled instead of fried, avoid high-carbohydrate foods—and in this way keep your arteries free from damaging deposits of cholesterol.

We know that an abundance of vitamin C strengthens the artery walls and aids in reducing high blood pressure; also, that calcium, vitamin E, and the B-complex vitamins are of vital importance to the health of your heart.

In fact, the best way to take care of your heart is to take care of your general health. That means sound nutrition, a low-fat,

low-carbohydrate diet, and a vitamin-mineral food supplement*—
even for that fine physical specimen, the somatotonia personality
type, who may think he doesn't need it!

The thin, delicate man or woman with the youthful, immature
appearance is a member of Dr. Sheldon's third group of physical
personalities, the *cerebrotonia*.

Are you this type?

Then you are dominated by the brain and the nervous system.
You wince at the noise of a crowd, and become so disturbed by
boisterousness that you tend toward introversion in an attempt
to find solitude. You have a different ductless gland make-up—
your adrenals and thyroid have a tendency to be overactive. You
are tense, nervous, and easily overstimulated. You require extra
rest and relaxation to slow down those glands. Even with an
adequate amount of proteins, vitamins, and minerals in your
diet, you will be undernourished, irritable, and generally below
par unless you are *fortified daily with a vitamin-mineral food
supplement*.

Your energy needs are high, but your body runs with a considerable amount of waste because of a lack of absorption. Dr. L.
Jean Bogert says of this type, "They have an unusually short and
muscularly active digestive tract, which may hurry food through
the body before it's completely digested and absorbed. Their
digestive systems are relatively inefficient, *and not all of the food
that they eat is made available to the body*."

Buttermilk, with its easily absorbed calcium, is a good between-
meal drink for you, and honey (in beverages) is a quick ener-
gizer. The foods that you eat *must supply the nutritive needs of
your body in ample quantity*, as you have less endurance than
the other types, and special precautions are needed to insure
adequate nourishment for you.

---

* A vitamin-mineral food supplement that I find thoroughly satisfactory for
my own use is called Nutri-Time. You might look into it. It is available in
most health-food stores.

"Each of these personality types," I told Dave, "must have the high-protein, tissue-building foods every day, whether he's the viscerotonic (the stomach man), the somatotonic (the muscle man), or the cerebrotonic (the nerve and brain man). The basic nutritional principles vary in degree only—not in kind."

"So I'm the stomach man?" asked Dave.

"Decidedly," I said.

"No doubt about it?" he asked.

"Not the slightest," I replied.

Dave looked down at his paunch and sighed, "I guess you're right. But I'm always tired. I have to eat the way I do for pep."

"You think so?" I asked. "Since I've been here, you've gorged yourself on several thousand calories of high-carbohydrate food. You've had one nap between plates of food, and you've rested constantly. How do you feel now?"

"Worn out," he admitted. "Too tired to move."

I looked over at the badminton court where Will was playing with the Nelson teen-agers. He moved with the speed and energy of any of the youngsters, and he seemed to be enjoying himself as much as they were. Dave's eyes followed mine, and I didn't need to say anything. The comparison was all too obvious.

It was then that he asked the inevitable question, "What's wrong with me?"

"You're a victim of your own body type and a diet of fats, sweets, and starches," I said. "Also I strongly suspect that you're anemic."

"Me? Anemic?" he asked. "How could I be anemic when I'm as fat as I am?"

"I don't know what caused the erroneous belief that only thin people are anemic. It's been found that a majority of overweight people are anywhere from slightly to seriously anemic. In such cases, food isn't utilized by the cells as it should be—it's piled on the body in layers of fat. Often overweight is corrected when anemia is cured, as the blood will then carry a maximum of nourishment to the cells from a minimum intake of food."

"I'm hungry most of the time," Dave said, "in spite of what I eat."

"Not in spite of what you eat," I said, "but *because* of it. You can eat quantities of the wrong food, such as you've been existing on, and still suffer from hidden hunger because your cells and tissues are starved for proteins, vitamins, and minerals. And in anemia the blood is deprived of the oxygen-carrying red corpuscles or hemoglobin. An anemic person may eat what he considers adequate meals, yet his body may be slowly starving because his blood isn't equipped with sufficient nutrient carriers or conveyers (red blood cells or hemoglobin) to pick up and carry the nourishment for which his hungry cells are pleading."

"Do I have to go on a special diet?" asked Dave.

"Let's say instead that you must make specific changes in your diet," I said. "Cut out all this junk—there's no other word for it!—that you've been eating and put yourself on the complete proteins of meat, eggs, fish, and dairy products. There's low-calorie cottage cheese that's all right for you, and powdered skim milk has all the protein and mineral content that whole milk has, minus the butterfat. To build red blood cells eat the organ meats whenever possible: liver, kidney, heart, and sweetbreads. Lean beef and the dark meat of poultry are rich in iron. Apricots are especially good as an added source of iron. So are citrus fruits and parsley, raisins, beets, whole grains, prunes, pineapple, and many other fresh, raw fruits and vegetables."

"I'm getting hungry again," said Dave, "just thinking of all those things."

"Add to food such as this a vitamin supplement rich in vitamin C and the B-complex group," I said, "along with minerals to supplement the foods rich in copper and iron, which you must have for the blood-building process."

The slanting rays of the late afternoon sun were beginning to filter through the shade of the oak leaves. Dave took out his dark glasses and put them on. "Can't stand the bright light in my eyes," he remarked.

"You'll find your eyes will improve on your high-protein diet," I said. "Protein is essential for the tone and elasticity of your eyes, and a lack of it is one of the contributing causes of cataract. Vitamin A is necessary for the health of your eyelids and the delicate tissues surrounding your eyes as well as for your visual purple, which is necessary for night vision. Eye fatigue, inflammation, and even the annoying twitching of your eyes are often due to an advanced deficiency of vitamin A. A more serious deficiency leads to xerophthalmia, or *dry eye.*"

"Looks like I've been kidding myself," said Dave. "Every time I wanted to read I felt like the fellow who said his eyes were all right—his arms just weren't long enough."

"To prevent farsightedness," I explained, "you should be sure that your diet contains plenty of calcium, vitamin D, and—you guessed it!—protein again. You need riboflavin to prevent twilight blindness and vitamin C for the lens of the eye."

"I'm beginning to see why you always recommend a multiple vitamin-mineral food supplement. It looks as though I need a lot of different vitamins for all of my deficiencies."

"I can give you an example," I said, "of a large-scale deficiency right here in your own State of Michigan. In 1923 an iodine deficiency caused as high an incidence of goiter as 47.2 per cent among 31,000 school children who were examined. But since the mineral iodine has been widely supplemented in the diet, by 1951 the incidence of goiter dropped to 1.4 per cent."

"Why should there be so much goiter in Michigan?" asked Dave.

"Because the local soil in which the food is grown lacks iodine," I said, "and ocean fish and seafoods, good sources of iodine, are not obtainable here. Other soils have other mineral deficiencies. That's why eating fruits and vegetables may not always protect you from a food deficiency."

Fatigue (especially chronic fatigue) is a warning signal that you're not feeding yourself properly. You can't erase this type of fatigue with sleep or rest until you build up your blood and body with the maximum quality of food. And this doesn't mean the maximum *amount* of food!

Following in the wake of this fatigue that comes from poor nutrition are the organic ills that destroy your physical and emotional personality. *Diseases come from the chemical failure of the body.*

If you have been fortunate enough to inherit a good chemical balance, a continued protein, vitamin, and mineral deficiency in your diet will, at best, cause early degeneration of your body's cells and resultant senility. But if you were born with partial genetic blocks due to a chemical imbalance in your body, then poor nutrition will invite the early onset of chronic disease. The chemistry of the body is extremely complex, and seldom is the balance perfect.

"Most of us," I told Dave, "are the victims of the *weak links* we are born with, or that we create in our bodies through neglect and abuse. That's the genetotrophic theory of disease—the recognition of the fact that even among normal persons there exist distinctive individual variations in metabolic patterns, or simply the manner in which your body is able to use the food that you eat."

"And doesn't that bring us right back to the personality types," Dave asked, "and the way each is affected by what he eats?"

"It does indeed," I said, "and do you remember what type you are?"

"I'm the stomach man," he said. "You know, I could learn to dislike that name."

"No one, of course, is an absolute type," I said. "There are variations in each."

"By taking advantage of the things you've told me about," Dave said, "and adding a little will power of my own, here's one stomach man who's going to vary his type!"

3

Your Emotional Personality

WHEN do your emotions start influencing your personality? They start playing a part in its development long before you are able to walk or talk. By the time you are three years old you have already formed many of your emotional reactions to life situations. Your personality development is a continuing process from then on.

"I don't know what's wrong with Jerry," Ellen Roberts complained to me about her three-year-old son. "He just won't eat by himself any more, and with a new baby to care for, I don't have time to feed him."

A new baby! There was the crux of little Jerry's emotional problem. His place had been usurped by the baby. When a child becomes emotionally disturbed, he expresses his unconscious rebellion in a way that demands the most attention from his parents. In Jerry's case, it was by refusing to eat.

By refusing his food at the table, Jerry found that his mother and father, in coaxing him to eat, paid him a little more longed-for attention than he had been getting.

"Do you let Jerry eat between meals?" I asked.

"Well, yes," she said. "When he gets hungry and begs for something I do. If I don't, he's big enough now to open the refrigerator or climb on a chair and reach the cooky jar himself."

"You must put a stop to this immediately," I said. "How can he have a real appetite at mealtime if he's allowed to help himself to cookies and sweets between meals? If you don't see that Jerry gets the balanced diet so necessary for his health, as well as his share of your time and love, you may make a neurotic personality out of the child."

"How could a three-year-old boy be neurotic?" she asked. "A child isn't born a neurotic!"

"No," I said. "But psychologists warn us that neurotics are partly born and partly made. The parents, for good or ill, finish the job. And you are allowing Jerry to regress to the infantile stage of the baby when he is hand-fed. How long he will continue this regression to the infantile stages of his life—to demand attention from you!—depends largely upon your wisdom and judgment. The fact is, he's already setting a bad personality pattern."

"He used to be such a happy, affectionate, obedient little boy," she said. "It's almost unbelievable, but his personality *has* changed. He's become sullen, rebellious, and—well, almost hostile at times."

"He feels insecure," I said. "His place has been taken by the baby, and the only way he can gain your attention is by dis-obedience in some form. A scolding is a poor substitute for a kiss, but it's better than nothing."

"Then you think parents are responsible for neurotic children?" she asked.

"Both parents are, to some extent," I said. "But the mother is directly responsible for her baby's mental and physical health from the very moment that it's conceived. The child who is born with a tendency to become neurotic is often high-strung, of a delicate constitution, and extremely sensitive to environmental deficiencies. So, while both parents give the child its heredity, it's the nutrition of the mother during pregnancy which influences her own health and that of her child. Also, as I've mentioned before, it's been proved that the mothers who are well-nourished and vitamin-fed during pregnancy, produce brighter babies."

Recent investigations at the medical schools of Toronto and Harvard universities offer evidence of a direct relationship between quality of the prenatal diet and welfare of both mother and child. The Harvard report was: "A higher proportion of babies whose condition was rated at birth as superior or good were born to mothers who had good or excellent diets during pregnancy."

"Then you believe in what our grandmothers used to call 'eating for two?'" asked Ellen.

"Only in terms of quality," I said, "which means the complete proteins of meat, fowl, eggs, and dairy products, the vitamins and minerals of fresh vegetables and fruits, plus a vitamin-mineral food supplement. This doesn't mean an exaggerated *quantity* of food."

"How can I get Jerry over this emotional disturbance," she asked, "so that he'll start eating and behaving normally again?"

"Jerry, like any child," I said, "was born with the need for love. You parents are responsible for the emotional health of your children—you teach them how to love or how to hate. Love paves the way to emotional adjustment; hate leads to neurosis. Love is born when the baby rests in your arms. As you feed and fondle him, he responds instinctively with his love. Even a tiny infant has the capacity to love those who show love for him. Love is so much a part of rearing your baby that he may sicken and die without it."

The documentary provided by Dr. Rene A. Spitz tells the pathetic story of ninety-seven babies in an orphanage. The babies were fed with regularity, but the nurses had no time to fondle and love them, and many of the infants died from the lack of love.

"But I love Jerry," Ellen protested. "I've just been too busy with the baby to pay much attention to him."

"Jerry is too young to understand why he isn't loved," I said. "At the age of three, all of his actions are guided by his emotions —and his emotion of jealousy comes from the feeling that the baby has taken his place."

Dr. Ernest Haase, the University of Illinois psychiatrist, says that neurosis begins building on the unstable soil of a delicate constitution with the early impressions and suggestions, the early acquired reflexes, *and the defenses and attitudes formed in early childhood.*

Most of our American heroes were individual, original, and self-assertive personalities. Lincoln had what psychologists call a *gyroscopic* personality, which enabled him to maintain his equilibrium (or his homeostasis) in the face of criticism. Today you teach your children that they must be aggressive in the struggle for survival, and in the same breath preach humility, courtesy, and consideration for everyone. You tell them that they must be rugged individualists, yet caution them that they have to conform or adjust to be accepted and popular.

"Today's child has no choice but to become hypocritical, cynical—or neurotic," Dr. Haase tells us.

Temperament is the raw stuff of individuality which is even independent of environment. Only when your inborn temperament is refined by your education and your growth does it become your personality.

"What can I do," Ellen asked, "to start building a good emotional personality for Jerry?"

"First," I said, "throw away the cooky jar and stop his habit of raiding the icebox so he'll begin eating regular, well-balanced meals again. A healthy child has a much easier time adjusting than a delicate one. Show an interest in what he does, share his fun and his little griefs, and let him feel loved and necessary to you again. Through good nutrition you can build the foundation for his health, personality, and future accomplishments. It's the sturdy, well-adjusted child, and not the frail bookworm, who consistently scores high in intelligence tests. The Princeton football great, Dick Kazmeier, was also an honor student."

"Throwing away the cooky jar," said Ellen, "will take a little will power. We're all fond of cookies and other sweets."

"If you allow him to eat sweets and starches between meals," I said, "you deprive him of the tissue-building materials—especially protein, calcium, and iron—which he should get at mealtime. These are absolutely necessary to build a strong, well-proportioned body with firm muscles, sound bones and teeth, plenty of red corpuscles in the blood, a digestive tract which functions smoothly, a high resistance to bacterial infections, a stable nervous system, and a happy disposition."

Dr. Agnes Fay Morgan, of the University of California, found that just the addition of wheat germ in the diet of a number of undernourished children brought about superior growth, fewer behavior problems, and improved mental alertness.

Glutamic acid, one of the amino acids of protein, produced many personality changes in the Columbia University experiments. The children scored higher on their intelligence tests after only a few months of treatment with glutamic acid. By superior nutrition, the personality can be lifted to a higher level of accomplishment than would normally be indicated by a child's heredity.

Poor nutrition in the crucial developmental years of childhood produces inferior personalities—physically, mentally, and emotionally. Continued dietary deficiencies make it difficult (if not impossible!) for the victim of hidden starvation to rise above mediocrity. The lack of proper food not only contributes to the deterioration of the personality—it may also precipitate a neurotic condition.

The human body has ways of saying "I am hungry" that range from hunger pains to disease and emotional upsets. Irritable, nervous outbursts are frequent telltale signs of the starved personality.

Ellen Roberts looked at her watch and jumped to her feet. "I must hurry home," she said. "There's so much to do—throw away the cookies, put a padlock on the refrigerator, and devote a little time and attention to Jerry—even if it means letting the baby cry a tiny bit!"

In all competitive sports emotion plays a big part. Remember Helen Wills, the tennis champion of some years ago? Helen was a pretty girl and a fine player, but so devoid of emotion that her audience never cared whether she won or lost. The sports writers had a rough time trying to make good, exciting copy out of her until one of them, in desperation, dubbed her Little Poker Face. That caught the public's fancy. At once she became to them the brave little girl who, win or lose, refused to show her emotions—instead of the colorless player who simply wasn't feeling *anything*.

From then on she became good copy for the newspapers. Almost as good (but not quite!) as Gussie Moran and her more recent display of lace-trimmed panties during a tennis tournament.

It isn't difficult to understand why the less proficient Gussie drew a bigger audience than Helen did. Which would *you* prefer to see on a tennis court—a poker face or lace-trimmed panties?

The question is irrelevant. You needn't answer it!

During the 1933 baseball season the New York Giants were stumbling in their quest for the pennant, and seemed beset by bad luck and various injuries. Then an unknown infielder from the minors sent them a few words of emotional encouragement.

"Don't worry," infielder Blondy Ryan telegraphed the wounded Giant team, "I'm on my way!"

And by some strange alchemy, the Giants got on *their* way. The telegram seemed to pep them up, and the New York Giants romped their way to the pennant and World Championship that year.

Baseball teams no longer ignore the emotional personality. The St. Louis Browns (now the Baltimore Orioles) once hired a psychologist to pull the team out of a slump. More attention is being paid to the mass mind of the fans and its effect on the team's fortunes. This is the era when a baseball manager is called upon to do everything, from pulling the men out of their inexplicable hitting slumps to influencing mob psychology.

When I first met Sol Harris he was one of those baseball enthusiasts who yelled, "Kill the umpire!" The unusual thing was, Sol really meant it—at least at the moment. He was a complex personality, tense and easily agitated, who had piled on emotional experience after emotional experience through all of his forty years. His personality was the product of the sensations he had gathered, of his opinions, impressions, desires, hopes, fears, thrills, and pain.

My office is quiet and relaxing, yet Sol was anything but relaxed as he sat before me. Thin, hunched over, and drumming frantically on the desk with nervous fingers, he presented a pathetic picture of personality degeneration, both physical and emotional.

"I'm afraid," he told me, "I'm headed for a nervous breakdown."

"What's the anxiety that seems to be driving you?" I asked.

"Most of my life," Sol began, "I've lived on my emotions, and now they've gotten the whip hand. Little things that I used to do automatically, or not at all, now have to be done religiously or I feel upset."

"They've become more or less of a ritual?" I asked.

"That's it," he said. "I have to drive the same way to work every day for fear I'll lose my way. I take several baths a day for fear of being unclean, and I'm afraid to leave the office at night until my desk is completely cleared." He stopped drumming long enough to light a cigarette. "I'm so bogged down with these trivial details which I'm compelled to do that I can't even think straight."

"And the greater your frustration, the more rigidly you observe your ritual," I added. "Your emotions take precedence over reason."

"The worst time," Sol stated, "is when I have a big job to finish or a decision to make. Then all these details heckle me."

"Decisions are hard for the emotional personality to make," I explained. "Life's decisions entail a continuous struggle between principle and expediency, between maturity and the evasions of childishness. You can't make good decisions if you're afraid and anxious."

"*That's* the trouble," Sol said, "I'm afraid. Just plain scared. Scared of everything." He wiped the beads of perspiration from his forehead, and looked around in the corners of the room as though something might be lurking there. "I'm afraid to face facts, so I can't decide what to do—and I never get anything done."

"No, you'd rather escape," I pointed out. "And for the emotional personality there are dozens of escape routes. Life on all fronts is a constant battle between acquisition and attrition. During these years when your emotions have been exposed to anxieties and fears, your body cells have been dying. Have you replaced them by eating a complete diet?"

"By a which?" asked Sol.

"You know," I said, "food. Nourishment, sustenance, groceries— remember them?"

"Oh, *food*," he repeated. "I can take it or leave it alone. Never did have much of an appetite. But here I am, a nervous wreck, and you talk to me about *groceries*."

"All right," I said. "We'll take that up later. You aren't able to face life because of ill health, both physical and emotional. So what do you do? You escape from pressure by extroversion, or the device of great activity. Your ritual of detail provides that escape for you."

Other escape routes used by the emotional personality under pressure are:

Regression to childhood patterns, so that someone else will bear the brunt of any real problems, as your parents once did.

Rationalization, or the device of kidding yourself by saying, "Say it isn't so."

Fixation, the divorcement of your spiritual life from your daily, business life is an example.

Repression, or forgetfulness, the emotional device of looking away from your problem, hoping in vain that it will disappear.

Projection, the device of blaming another person or thing for your own mistakes.

Don't blame the failure of your personality on your friends, fate, circumstances, or the stars. Shakespeare, that amazing chronicler of human experience, scoffed at the strong belief in astrology which was prevalent in the seventeenth century by saying, "The fault, dear Brutus, is not in our stars, but in ourselves that we are underlings." And again, in *King Lear*, "An admirable evasion of whoremaster man, to lay his goatish disposition to the charge of a star!"

Although they were unknown in his time, in those few words Shakespeare defined the neurotic devices of Projection or Scapegoatism.

"What am I going to do to get out of this ritualistic rut?"

"Your extroversion," I said, "your device of great activity, doesn't help you a bit unless it is related to the problems you are trying to solve. At this point, I would suggest you try a direct route to good emotional health."

"I'll need a road map for that route," said Sol. "I don't know the way."

"First," I instructed him, "improve your physical condition so you'll have the stamina to face reality. The B vitamins so greatly aid a person in becoming emotionally mature and integrated that they've been called the "courage vitamins." Your jangling nerves and erratic compulsions are a warning that your body is hungering for *all* the important vitamins and minerals contained in a good vitamin-mineral food supplement, plus three protein-rich meals a day—eggs, meat, fish, poultry, or cheese with every meal."

"Every meal?" Sol groaned. "I don't eat that much in a week!"

"You'd better," I warned, "from this day on for the rest of your life. You can't solve your problems by behaving like Jubilation T. Cornpone (in *Li'l Abner*, the musical comedy) and galloping resolutely off in the wrong direction—which is just what you've been doing."

"I guess I have, at that," admitted Sol. "I never paid any attention to vitamins."

"Don't forget the minerals," I said, "if you want to keep your nervous system in good order. If you lack magnesium in your diet, your behavior may become eccentric and irrational—even bordering on the psychotic."

"That sounds like my case history," he replied. "Where do I get these minerals?"

"In the well-balanced diet that you're starting on immediately," I said. "But to insure adequate amounts, I always recommend a good vitamin-mineral food supplement. And don't get the impression, as many people do, that you can skip meals and get by as long as you're taking the supplement. The two work together to promote better health, with steadier nerves and an improved personality. Calcium and magnesium help your tense and jangled nerves to relax, and sunshine, a source of vitamin D, aids your body's absorption of calcium. The lactic acid and calcium in buttermilk make it a desirable drink, especially at bedtime if you need a sleep inducer."

"I'll try anything once," said Sol. "What can I lose?"

"You can't lose a thing," I assured him, "and you stand to gain a whole new life, a different mental outlook, a stronger body, and a more vital personality. Your ability to think rationally will return. You'll find you can sit down and take time to deliberate the solutions to your problems. Use your nerves for a keener awareness, a greater satisfaction and enrichment of your life."

"My life could certainly use a little enrichment," said Sol.

"The amount of satisfaction you get from life," I said, "depends largely on your own ingenuity, self-sufficiency, and resourcefulness. You emotional personalities must avoid scattering your nervous energies on trivialities. Stop doing all the unnecessary things that waste your time and strength—the activity devices—and save your energy for important undertakings."

Dr. Hans Selye tells us that each exposure to stress leaves an indelible scar. Acute fatigue is a form of stress which may be combatted with proper rest and relaxation, combined with good nutrition. While what Dr. Selye calls superficial adaptation energy can be restored, enabling you to go about the business of living once more, your consuming of that deeper "frozen reserve" of vitality, year in and year out, is what ages you.

"Your ability to adapt to various experiences," I went on, "determines whether or not the stresses you encounter daily in work, love, or marriage are prolonged and injurious, causing the body to break down, or whether they are mild and temporary in their effect. It's fine to be keyed up when you have to meet a stress situation head-on. But it's absolutely disastrous to your mind, body, and personality to stay keyed up continually, which you have a bad habit of doing."

Dr. Selye also says, "In all our actions throughout the day, we must constantly look for signs of being keyed up too much—and we must learn to stop in time. To watch our critical stress level is as important as to watch our critical quota of cocktails. More so."

"I've always been sort of a physical weakling," said Sol, "which may account for my emotional upsets."

"If you face your health needs and do something about them," I said, "you can build on your weaknesses until they become a strength. Two of our great presidents, Theodore and Franklin Roosevelt, were inspiring examples of this: the one, a sickly child who grew up to be the 'bull moose' who led the charge up San Juan Hill; the other, a polio-stricken adult, who refused to be crippled mentally or spiritually. Two famous heavyweight boxers, James J. Corbett and Gene Tunney were both tubercular in their childhood. And you're old enough to remember Eugene Sandow, but you may not know that he was a weakling who overcame his handicaps to become a great athlete."

"You know," said Sol, "if so many other guys can do it, what's to prevent me?" His cigarette had gone out, but he didn't light another one. The nervous hands were still, and the sudden laughter that came from his lips was easy and relaxed. "Me and Eugene Sandow—how do you like that?"

"Just as you said," I told him, "what's to prevent you? As your physical and mental health improve—and they soon will, with

your three protein-rich meals and vitamin-mineral food supplement—you'll find that you'll no longer use escape devices, and
you'll be better equipped to cope with your problems."

"Problems?" asked Sol. "What problems?"

"The ones that were weighing you down when you walked
into my office," I said, "before we started talking them out."

"Oh, those!" he said. "It's a funny thing, but they don't seem
insurmountable now. In fact, if you asked me right this minute—
I couldn't even tell you what they were!"

4

Your Mental Personality

"COME into the library," Stan Martin said, "so we can have some privacy. Nobody ever uses it any more."

He opened the door and we entered a book-lined room, dark and dusty with disuse.

"I can see," I said, "that your library isn't the popular place it used to be when anybody looking for you could always find you here."

"That was fifteen years ago," he said, raising the shades and letting in some light, "when I was in college. I was pretty much of a grind then. But I've hardly had time to open a book since."

I remembered the Stan Martin of college days: brilliant, eager, and vital, an outstanding student and a member of Phi Beta Kappa. He bore little resemblance to the man who sank into the chair opposite mine and passed a hand across his dazed and bloodshot eyes.

"Have you been ill, Stan?" I asked.

"Not exactly," he said. "And I haven't been drinking, either. But I'm as foggy as a punch-drunk fighter. Can't even think straight any more. I suppose I've really been slipping on the job for quite a while, but I didn't realize it until I failed to pass an executive test the company gave. I missed out on a promotion that could have been mine. And I can't understand yet why I failed that test, which should have been easy for me."

"Do you mind if I raise a window?" I asked. "It seems a little stuffy in here."

"Sure, sure," he said, "go right ahead." His next words, when they came, were slow and halting, as though the effort to think was far too much for him. "But don't expect a breeze to blow away my mental fog. It goes deeper than that. I'm afraid I'm losing the best asset I ever had—my mental power. That is, if I haven't already lost it."

"There are several things," I said, "that could help explain your difficulty. But first, let's examine a few facts about you. You don't look as though you've taken any care of your health."

"Never paid much attention to it," he said, "as long as I could keep going on strong coffee—and I usually did. I realize I've never been the huskiest guy in the world, but what's my health got to do with my losing the ability to think coherently?"

"You started out in life as a highly gifted person, Stan," I said. "Now, it's presumed that the highly gifted person has some inborn capacity to co-ordinate the electrical circuits in his brain unusually well. The more you exercise the function of combining the hundreds of circuits into larger ones, the easier it is for these circuits to work, the more extensive they become, and the more your mind develops."

"Not *my* mind," said Stan. "It stopped developing in college."

"Then you haven't been using it the way you used to," I said. "To no other part of your body is the saying 'to rest is to rust' more applicable. Have you made any conscious efforts to keep learning since you graduated?"

"No," he answered, "nor unconscious ones, either. I suppose, like any bright college lad, I thought I learned enough in college to last me a lifetime. And now, after all these years, my learning days are over."

"Only if you've lost the desire to learn," I said. "I know a man who started his college education at the age of seventy-nine."

"He must have been an exceptional old man," said Stan.

"He was, indeed," I affirmed. "And nobody ever thought of

calling Major Richard R. Vincent old. In 1885, at the age of nine, he completed McGuffey's third grade reader in Cleveland, Ohio. That was all the formal schooling he had until seventy years later, as a retired major, he entered a special program for students who didn't have high school diplomas—and began his college career in the Columbia University School of General Studies."

But the major's *informal* education had continued during his seventy years between classes. He had mushed a dog sled across the Yukon, and had fallen into the crater of Kilauea Volcano in Hawaii. At one time or another, he had fought Philippine savages, strung telephone wires across the head-hunter country in Brazil, and survived tsetse fly bites in Africa. He participated in the pursuit of Pancho Villa in Mexico, his army career included four wars, and he was at home in such faraway places as Mongolia, Siberia, Tibet, Kashmir, and the South Sea Islands.

"I can see," said Stan, "that this seventy-nine-year-old college boy never gave himself a chance to become mentally stagnant."

"Not only that," I said, "he remained a colorful and interesting personality because he was continually learning something new. He never allowed his brain to deteriorate through atrophy of the brain's nerve cells."

"Do you think if you don't continue using your brain that it loses its ability to function?" asked Stan.

"Look at it this way," I said. "Learning is associated with the ability to create new, reverberating electrical circuits in the brain. Most successful men keep creating and extending their electrical circuits throughout life. By maintaining his mental powers, a man can continue to acquire new knowledge and skills for as long as he lives. The late Toscanini, because of failing eyesight, was unable to read the scores of the great symphonies that he conducted, so he memorized them! Your brain never wears out through use. It may degenerate as you get older from *dis*use or nutritional starvation—or both."

Your brain receives its electrical impressions from about one million nerve fibers which lead to it. To protect you from an avalanche of impressions that would be overwhelming, an impression must be strong enough to command cellular response before it reaches the main message centers in the brain.

"If you want to make maximum use of your brain," I went on, "keep those electrical circuits open and operating through constant use."

"My nerves have been pretty ragged," Stan said. "Would that affect my brain?"

"More than anything else," I said, "except the brain's food supply. When your nervous system becomes damaged it interferes with the functioning of your brain, which is dependent upon the nervous system for communication with the other parts of the body. The electrical impressions from your nerve fibers must be strong enough to jump across the tiny gaps (synapses) in your nervous system. If you let these electrical circuits get out of control, your brain reacts with excessive anxiety, ungovernable rage, or other irrational states of mind."

"I'm beginning to see why you asked about my health," Stan admitted. "It looks as though my nerves and brain are both dependent on it."

"They are," I said. "And if you want your brain to function as it should, you must avoid any damage that might occur through starvation of the brain cells."

"In what way," asked Stan, "are brain cells starved?"

"The way that we're most familiar with," I answered, "is the cerebral vascular accident, an accident in one of the blood vessels of the brain which shuts down the flow of blood temporarily to the area of Broca. As soon as adequate blood flow is restored to the oxygen-starved cells, the patient is on the road to recovery. In elderly patients who have arteriosclerosis, there is usually an involvement of the brain's arteries which have become inelastic and narrowed, offering points of resistance that invite clot formation. The same thing happens in younger men who are suffering from atherosclerosis, a condition in which the arteries become clogged with cholesterol."

"I know," said Stan. "I used to think that was just an old man's disease. But not any more! I know too many fellows my age and younger who have it."

"Yes," I said, "and besides the results of vascular spasms or strokes, a definite relationship exists between cerebral circulation and brain activity."

What is sometimes called "senile softening of the brain" is actually a clogging up of the cerebral arteries caused by the same cholesterol deposits that are now known to damage the heart. These clogged cerebral arteries decrease circulation of blood to the brain. In such an unfavorable condition, one can expect something to happen to the brain . . . anything from senility to a stroke that cripples or kills.

"Isn't there some preventive measure for this?" Stan wanted to know.

"A balanced diet *very low* in both fats and carbohydrates is an absolute necessity," I stressed. "And, to burn up those accumulated cholesterol deposits—or to prevent them—you really should make lecithin a part of your daily diet."

"Lecithin? Is that something new?" Stan asked. "I never heard of it."

"Not really new," I replied. "It's been around for quite some time, but only in recent years has it gained a new appreciation. Lecithin is something that I firmly believe every man should use. It's a homogenizing agent that's capable of breaking up fat and cholesterol into tiny particles that can be absorbed by the tissues."

The celebrated Dr. Lester M. Morrison, in writing about lecithin, calls it the greatest nutritional development of the last fifty years. In telling about his patients who used lecithin, Dr. Morrison said: "They had more vitality, did not grow tired so quickly as they had formerly, and were in better general health than before." Certainly such chemicophysical benefits cannot help but have a favorable influence on personality, general attitude toward others—to say nothing of improved brain function.

"It is my firm belief that every man should use lecithin daily," I said. "For his health, his nerves, his manhood—"

At this point Stan interrupted with: "Lecithin, huh? For my health, my nerves, and my manhood. I'd better look into this!"

"We were talking about your brain—remember?" I said.

"I know, I know. But this other deal intrigues me . . . even more than how not to starve my brain cells."

"I'm glad you got back to the original subject," I said. "There *is* another way you can starve your brain cells—through a lack of oxygen. You can injure the brain if you withhold enough oxygen from it, as in the case of carbon monoxide poisoning. It's the slow starvation, however, that lowers your intelligence and ability. The hemoglobin in your blood carries oxygen to your brain, just as it does to your muscles and tissues, and your body manufactures these red corpuscles out of proteins and iron. *If you fail to give your body enough of these blood-building materials, you deprive your brain of its most important substance, oxygen.*"

"You said something about the brain's food supply," said Stan. "What did you mean by that?"

"Your brain's nourishment is exclusively blood sugar, or glucose," I said. "Your brain isn't able to store sugar for future use, as other parts of your body can. Instead, for proper functioning, it is absolutely dependent upon its moment-to-moment blood-sugar level."

"What happens, then," asked Stan, "if your brain doesn't get enough of this blood sugar?"

"Your mental personality changes," I said. "You suffer the symptoms of hyperinsulinism, which are hunger, weakness, fatigue, anxiety and nervousness—even crying spells— a tremulous feeling, motor in-co-ordination, mental confusion and disorientation, a low muttering delirium, and in the more severe cases, stupor."

"A stupor," said Stan, "is just what I've been in. So maybe you'd better tell me just how to keep my brain supplied with this stuff that's so essential."

"You maintain a constant level by eating the foods that will keep your blood sugar on an even keel," I said. "These foods are proteins, *and not sugar or sweets,* as many persons erroneously believe."

Dr. G. W. Thorn and his co-workers at Harvard University found, in experiments to determine blood-sugar levels, that a high-protein meal of skimmed milk, lean ground beef, and cottage cheese boosted the blood-sugar level slowly to the high level of 120 milligrams, where it remained throughout the following six hours.

"I wonder," said Stan, "what the effect of my breakfast of sweet rolls and coffee would be."

"According to experiments by scientists in the United States Department of Agriculture," I replied, "on such a breakfast your blood sugar would fall within an hour to a low level, resulting in inefficiency and fatigue. The more protein you eat for breakfast— eggs, meat, fish, nonfat milk, and cheese—the more you nourish your brain for its maximum efficiency."

Vitamins and minerals are desperately needed by the body to manufacture food for the brain. The minerals iron and copper are needed to produce hemoglobin. The thyroid gland, which affects your moods as well as your intelligence and initiative, requires a daily generous ration of iodine.

The excessive use of ordinary table salt may affect the brain adversely. Some doctors believe that an excessive salt intake can eventually cause migraine headaches and other types of cerebral disorders. Dr. Max Goldzieher attributes migraine headaches to cranial pressure caused by increased water flow to tiny blood vessels, due to abnormal retention of salt in the tissues.

"Are there any vitamins that help your brain functions?"

"If you want the name of a specific vitamin the lack of which can result in insanity," I said, "it's the B complex. But the most advisable thing for you to do is to take a complete, balanced vitamin-mineral food supplement. And, of course, lecithin."

"Don't worry," said Stan, "I won't forget lecithin!"

"In that way," I said, "you can be sure that you're getting all the essential food elements needed by your brain to insure its adequate functioning. These, of course, are merely supplements to the protein-rich three meals a day that you're starting on immediately, beginning with that all-important meal, breakfast."

"I've gotten so confused and mixed up mentally," said Stan, "and in such a rut that it's been easier for me to do nothing than to try to think my way out of difficulties that require decisive action or sustained thought."

"A high-protein diet and nutritional supplements will keep your blood sugar at a high level," I said. "This will help you to concentrate for long periods at a time.

"But you may need to retrain yourself mentally if the rut is of long standing. You'll have to put aside all emotions such as self-pity, fear, and self-consciousness, unhealthy states of mind such as unrealism, and bad habits like laziness and slovenliness. These interfere with mental discipline and the ability to concentrate. Enthusiasm is a big factor in this. Don't allow your thoughts to be sidetracked by irrelevancies. If you feel that each particular task is of tremendous importance, then you'll work—and have fun doing it!—to see that it reaches fruition."

"I can't remember how long it's been," said Stan, "since my job, or anything else for that matter, has seemed to be fun. It's even hard for me to remember what the word means!"

"Nothing is any fun when you're constantly half-sick and sluggish because of malnutrition—so often the result of a high-carbohydrate diet—and inadequate rest. But if you give them a fighting chance, your body, mind, and personality will respond to the way you feed them in an inspiring fashion. A delight in living, a sense of accomplishment in your work, and increased happiness in your personal life are some of the rewards."

"Another bad habit I acquired at work," said Stan, "was that I let too many things distract me. The telephone, the clackety-clack of a typewriter, and the traffic noises in the street below. They all seemed to conspire to annoy me at the times when I especially needed the power of concentration."

"Thomas Edison was deaf, as you know," I said, "but he never regretted his deafness, for it enabled him to concentrate even in a noisy crowd. There are different types of mental personalities, which is fine, as each one can excel in his particular field. The introverts are generally found among scientific researchers, writers, and philosophers, to name a few. The extroverts among salesmen, business executives, and politicians. Of course the integrated personality—one with a balance of many personality types—adjusts best to the world, his fellow man, and myriad working conditions."

"Don't tell me," Stan said, "let me guess! All else being equal, the integrated personality is the fellow with the well-nourished body and mind."

"Exactly," I said. "He's the one who can tune out noise and minor annoyances and concentrate on the job at hand. The one whose thoughts are clear and constructive, because he hasn't starved his brain. He learns the facts of his problem, faces them, and considers them thoroughly to avoid snap judgment. He rules out any interfering emotions, makes his decision, and implements it."

"That's certainly been one of my troubles," Stan said, "letting my emotions interfere with my work."

"Naturally," I said, "your emotions do interfere, unless you control them. It's difficult to divorce your mental personality completely from your emotional personality, but you have to see to it that your emotions don't dominate your powers of reason."

"It's like the old saying about not letting your heart rule your head," Stan said, "and it looks as though I should start using my emotions less and my brain more."

"The brain," I said, "is the most underused part of the human body in most of us, even you."

"What do you mean, *even* me?" asked Stan. "Are you just too courteous to say *especially* me?"

"I might have made it a little stronger," I said, "except that I thought possibly you'd begin to resent so much frankness."

"I couldn't resent anything you've said to me," Stan said; "it's made too much sense, and it's offered me hope for what seemed like a hopeless situation. Do you think, after these years in a mental stupor, that I'll really be able to catch up with a world that was leaving me behind?"

"I haven't the slightest doubt of it," I said, "after you get your body and mind in a healthy condition to receive impressions. Then harness your unconscious mind and make it work for you."

Experiments in learning have proved that you can automatically condition your subconscious mind, which never sleeps and which is a vast storehouse for all the knowledge ever fed it. That knowledge is there, waiting to be tapped, as many students and almost all writers know. Robert Louis Stevenson spoke of it long ago. "When I write," he said, "it's as though a trap-door opens in my mind, and things I didn't know were in there come out."

"I think they use that subconscious method to teach languages now, don't they?" asked Stan.

"They do," I said, "and it has been most successful. You start studying (or in some cases, listening to records which continue playing after you've gone to sleep) before you go to bed, then during your sleeping hours your *tuned-in brain* absorbs the knowledge that's fed it."

"One of my teachers used to say, 'You can lead a boy to college, but you can't make him think,'" Stan said. "I kept remembering that and it worried me all this time when I couldn't even *make* myself think. Funny how a thing like that would stick in my subconscious."

"That's just what we were talking about," I said, "your subconscious never forgets a thing. Your mental power is still there to be reawakened, Stan. If you harness your subconscious and start using it, you'll be ready for that next promotion when it comes around."

"Why not?" Stan said, with his first show of confidence. "And maybe in time I'll get back the alertness, the ambition, and the whole mental personality of my younger days. Then, fortified with proteins, vitamins, and minerals—not forgetting lecithin!— maybe I'll even romp in to see the corporation president and tell him to give me another executive test—and to make it a tough one!"

5

Don't Let Your Neuroses Enslave You

I ENTERED my office to keep a ten o'clock appointment with Doris Norton. It was only 9:15, but my secretary had told me that Miss Norton arrived early and was waiting for me.

But the office was empty. Empty, did I say? Not quite. A cigarette was still smoldering in the ash tray. A white glove, twisted, knotted, and dropped in sudden panic, was on the floor.

From somewhere in the direction of the window drapes, I could hear labored breathing. I sat down at my desk and waited quietly, seemingly engrossed in the memos before me. This was evidently a badly disturbed girl, and I didn't want to frighten her away.

Finally, a thin, blue-veined hand pulled the drapes apart, and Miss Norton came into view, trembling yet defiant.

"This is all nonsense," she said. "My mother made the appointment. I didn't want to come here at all. I don't need your help. I don't need anybody's help."

"Then why," I asked, "did you arrive forty-five minutes early?"

"Because I'm punctual," she answered. "I'm reliable and trustworthy, no matter what anybody tells you. I do what must be done and get it over with."

I didn't tell her that, according to psychologists, being too early for an appointment was just as bad, or worse, than being too late; that the person who is habitually early is likely to be one with a strong feeling of insecurity. Nor did I mention that she was making too great an issue of her reliability, and that her defense mechanism was showing. I let her talk on.

"I don't know what *she* told you, but I'm positive there wasn't much truth in it," she said.

"If you mean your mother," I replied, "she told me very little. She preferred to let me draw my own conclusions."

"*She* isn't as dependable as I am. Perhaps I shouldn't say it about my own mother, but she's scatterbrained and inefficient and does nothing in life except get by on her charm—which I could never do."

Her breathing had become so difficult that she was talking in gasps. I poured a glass of water and said, "Here, drink this slowly—and just lean back and relax. There's nothing to be afraid of. Nothing at all. I'm going to help you."

She sipped the water and looked at me incredulously. "Why," she said, "I believe you *care* whether I'm sick or well—maybe even whether I live or die." Then, unaccountably, she burst into tears.

I set a box of tissues on the desk beside her, then walked over to the window and looked out. "Leave her alone for a little while with her real or fancied grief," I thought. "Let her cry herself out. It's what she needs."

After a few moments of uncontrolled sobbing, her breathing became less labored. Finally she wiped her eyes, straightened up, and took a deep breath. "My asthma," she said, "it—it's better. I can breathe now. What did you do to me?"

"I didn't do anything," I said. "You found some much-needed relief in tears. It must have been a long time since you've had a good cry."

"My mother always gets her way by turning on a few tears," she insisted, "but I never cry. I don't know what happened to me. Your unexpected kindness—your wanting to help me—I couldn't bear it."

"You say that," I said, "as though you're not used to kindness."

"Nobody," she said, "has ever been kind to me since my father died. I was nine years old then. My mother married again indecently soon, and I've had no use for her or my stepfather since that time. *She* saw to it that my father didn't leave me any money of my own until I'm twenty-five, so I have to live with them until then."

"Why don't you get a job and move out?" I asked.

"I can't," she answered. "My health won't permit it."

"All right," I told her, "now we're getting some place. *Why have you been deliberately starving yourself, both physically and emotionally, all these years?*"

She looked at me as though I had dealt her a mortal blow. "I don't know what you mean," she barely whispered.

"Is it to punish your mother in some indirect way, or are you deliberately trying to make yourself unattractive to men, so that none will intrude on the memory of your father?"

"Don't mention other men in the same breath with my father," she demanded.

"Don't you see what you're doing?" I asked. I took her cold, tense hand and led her over to a mirror. "Look in that mirror. What do you see?"

She looked at the large, expressive, but haunted eyes that stared back at her, at the emaciated cheeks and scrawny neck, hair skinned back in an unbecoming knot, and the pale, tight lips devoid of lipstick.

> "Mirror, mirror on the wall,
> Who's the homeliest girl of all?"

she mocked.

"You're not homely at all," I said, as she went back and huddled dejectedly in her chair. "Or at least you wouldn't have to be. You could be a very stunning and interesting looking girl. But you won't achieve it by feeling sorry for yourself, or being jealous of your mother—and most certainly not by clinging to the past instead of living in the present. You've let your neuroses enslave you. Your health, nerves, personality, and appearance have suffered. You can start now to do something about it, or you can go on as you are and wreck your whole life. The choice is yours. No one else can make it for you."

There was a long pause before she spoke. "I've always prided myself on my honesty, even when it hurt. And you're right. I seem to feel that there's some virtue in half-starving myself—in contrast to my mother's and stepfather's enjoyment of good food and luxury, which always seemed gross to me."

"And now," I said, "your body is so weak from malnutrition that you can't get rid of these negative thoughts. You've filled your mind with the sludge of fear, resentment, jealousy, hate, and overconcern with your physical inadequacy."

"But I *am* inadequate," she argued, "and not quite up to the struggle of living. If I ever try to make any plans, I never have the strength to carry them out. And I have no personality. You talked to my mother. She—sparkles. I couldn't sparkle if my life depended on it."

"First of all," I said, "you need to start a positive program to build up your health, strengthen your body, and relax your nerves. If you eat the type of food—and *enough* of it!—to do this, your personality will soon begin to emerge with a new glow and, perhaps, even a sparkle. As your personality develops, it enables you to change your life from one of dependence to one of mature independence."

"Independence?" she said. "Now, that's one thing I've—"

"I know, it's one thing you've always prided yourself on! But it would be a good idea, instead of priding yourself on so many estimable but grim virtues, to develop a little pliancy, more warmth, and responsiveness. When you came in here you told me that you didn't need my help, or anybody's help."

"I told you that," she said, "because I was frightened. I didn't think anybody could or would help me. But I've changed my mind. I trust you. Will you help me . . . please?"

"Of course I will," I said. "You mentioned your mother's sparkling personality, and also the fact that she enjoyed good food, which seemed gross to you."

It is impossible for a person who is chemically starved—nutritionally depleted—to have a pleasing personality. The chemicals in the body are living materials balanced in a harmonious nutritional symphony. If the natural chemical balance is disturbed, the body can become sick and the personality experiences emotional ups and downs.

When the chemical balance is lopsided, so is the personality. Correct the chemical balance, and the personality sparks up. Too many persons leave the chemical balance to chance, and if chance runs in a favorable groove, the emotional level is high. But when nutritional starvation creeps in, through carelessness or neglect, the emotional level may hit the lowest depths of dejection.

"It's absolutely impossible," Doris said, "for me to eat the amount of food that my mother and stepfather consume. Eggs every morning for breakfast, meat two and sometimes three times a day, besides an abundance of vegetables, fruit, and cheese. It's almost uncivilized."

"Then what we need," I said, "is more uncivilized people like them. That's exactly the way I want you to start eating. If you can't manage it in three meals a day, divide it up into five smaller meals. Your mother evidently knows the value of high-protein meals three times a day, plus the vitamin-rich and mineral-laden fresh fruits and vegetables."

"She is a good cook," she admitted, "and she's always reading things about nutrition, in your books and various articles."

"Then I don't need to tell you what you must eat," I said. "Simply eat the meals your mother prepares, which you have described, and eat them in ample quantity, including meat and eggs for breakfast."

"Meat for breakfast," she groaned, "is repulsive to me."

"A high-protein breakfast is necessary," I said, "to give you *specific dynamic action*—the action that enables you to get things done."   ,

"It's easier for me," she said, "to skip breakfast, and think about how I can't do something, rather than to make the effort to figure out how it can be done."

"That's one reason for your frustration," I pointed out. "You suffer pangs of conscience because you give up before you even try. Then you find it hard to live with yourself afterwards.

"Protein ingestion gives you a specific dynamic effect equivalent to 30 per cent of its caloric value, while carbohydrates and fats are only 6 per cent and 4 per cent respectively. Well-balanced, high-protein meals, plus a vitamin-mineral food supplement will build up your health. This, in turn, will ease your emotional tensions and give you the ability to follow the program of balanced living that's essential for your personality."

"The way you put it," Doris said, "if I don't make myself healthy physically by overcoming my aversion to food, my emotions cannot be healthy."

"They can't be," I said, "because you create a vicious circle for yourself. By not eating the foods that will keep your body healthy, you create a bad environment for your physical personality. You acquire ailments that make you emotionally unstable. With your mind in this unhealthy emotional state, you become unable to think clearly and constructively."

"Then by keeping my body healthy, you believe that I can control my emotions—my feelings of insecurity, failure, and inadequacy?" she asked.

"I do," I said, "for a healthy body is an adaptable body which can take the stresses and strains of life. Your personality is a very complex combination of your body, mind, and emotions, and none of these can properly function independently of the others. Your personality is at its best when you have the health to be mentally and physically active. Systematic physical activity serves to neutralize the tiring effects of mental fatigue. Mental and physical activity keep your emotions healthy."

"*Now* you want me to exercise!" she protested.

"Well, don't say it as though it's a naughty word," I said. "It certainly needn't be routine and boring. There used to be such a thing as walking for pleasure. Swimming, riding, golf, even the mild game of croquet. Exercise can be play, you know."

"I don't know how to play," said Doris. "My mother has always done all the frivolous playing in the family."

"Your mother," I said, "is a normal, healthy, integrated personality who has risen above her personal sorrow and made the best of her life. Why not recognize this fact, instead of resenting her happiness and being jealous of her?"

"I never said I was jealous of my mother."

"You don't have to say it," I said. "It has motivated your whole life. Because she's charming and attractive, you've convinced yourself that she's frivolous, and you've gone to the other extreme by becoming self-righteous and prim. Try to understand that she's a woman who loved your father as much as you did. Loved him too much, perhaps, to go on living without someone to take his place—something which you refused to do—so she married again, and you've let resentment of it cloud your whole life.

"If you want to know how grown-up emotionally you are, you might read these seven qualities listed by Dr. William C. Menninger, the noted psychiatrist, as criteria of emotional maturity." I handed her a typewritten card from my files, taken from Dr. Menninger's speech before the Bergen County Mental Health Center in Rochelle Park, New Jersey.

She took it without a word, and the office was quiet as she studied the following questions:

1. Can you change? (This implies the abandonment of solutions learned in childhood.)

2. Can you accept frustrations for future gain? (Ability to compromise rather than a running away or fighting.)

3. Can you find more satisfaction in giving than in getting? (A reversal of the infant role, which has only demands.)

4. Can you meet stress without disabling symptoms?

5. Can you direct your anger into constructive outlets?

6. Do you have the capacity to love? (Dr. Menninger says love is the only neutralizer of hate.)

7. Can you relate to people in a consistent manner? Or do you switch from friendliness today to hostility tomorrow?

Doris looked up from the list of questions into my eyes. Her own eyes were intense and pleading, but they were calm now; the pupils were no longer dilated as they had been. And since that first asthmatic attack, her breathing had been regular and rhythmic.

"I'm afraid," she said, "that my answer is no to all the questions. Disgraceful, isn't it?"

"Keep the list where you can see it often," I said. "And there's another Dr. Menninger, Karl, who wrote two books you should read—*Man Against Himself* and *Love Against Hate*. Perhaps they'll help you to find out why you've been so bent on your own self-destruction through semistarvation, and why you absolutely must love or perish."

"Love or perish," she said. "It sounds frightening, doesn't it?"

"Only if you're afraid of love," I said. "To me it sounds wonderful. I'd like to have it printed on banners and strung around the world."

"Do you think," she asked, "that if I improve my health it will increase my capacity to love?"

"I have no doubt of it," I replied. "Your emotions will become more stable, your personality more adaptable. The adaptable personality grows, loves, embraces new ideas, explores new developments, and is able to throw off the clutter of bad habits, emotional prejudices, and negative thoughts. In all building, you have to start with a good foundation. And a healthy body is the foundation of sound emotions and a vibrant personality."

Doris Norton put the list of questions in her purse and rose from her chair, unconsciously straightening her thin shoulders with a new pride and purpose.

Her eyes suddenly filled with an unexpected glint of humor. "I'm going home now," she said, "and eat every morsel of food that my mother puts on my plate. She'll be so surprised that she'll probably lose *her* appetite."

6

Can Your Personality
Weather a Storm?

IF YOU are an integrated personality, you can weather the emotional storms of life. You can take without flinching the figurative hailstones that beat upon your head in those dark days that come to all of us, when everything goes wrong and it seems that the sun will never shine again. Yours is essentially an optimistic and courageous nature.

The persons who coined the old adages, "The darkest hour is just before the dawn" and "Every cloud has a silver lining," were undoubtedly integrated personalities.

The weak, underfed, or defeated personality has a completely different outlook on life. He sees failure in temporary setbacks, his gloomy days outnumber by far the ones of fair weather, and a genuine storm or crisis results in panic for him. Misfortune seems heaped upon misfortune, and instead of meeting the challenge, he gives up in despair.

It was such a fellow as this who invented those other well-known sayings, "Misfortunes never come singly" and "It never rains but that it pours."

Scientists agree, however, that almost everyone's personality is affected to some extent by the weather. When the weather is clear and sunny, so are our moods and dispositions. We are more reliable workers and better companions, because our capacity for enjoyment of life is on a higher level.

But let it rain, storm, become foggy, gloomy, violent, or be in any way what one of my Southern friends calls "be-falling" weather, and what happens? Our capacity for enjoyment dwindles, and we feel with William Cullen Bryant that "the melancholy days are come, the saddest of the year."

Mark Twain once said, "Everybody talks about the weather, but nobody does anything about it."

But W. Wesley Hicks is trying!

He's a San Francisco manufacturer of electric heaters, who has pioneered studies in the United States on the effect of the weather upon your personality.

Mr. Hicks predicts, "We are on the verge of one of the great break-throughs in man's knowledge of himself and our atmosphere. The results could affect every living creature on earth."

Our personalities tend to vary directly with the barometer.

Normal barometric pressure at sea level is about 30. When the barometer reads 30 or more and rises or remains steady, our spirits do the same. The weather is clear and calm, and our moods correspond. But let the barometer drop below 30 and continue dropping, and we're in for a storm . . . of the elements and of the emotions. Our personality nose-dives with the barometer!

Have you ever noticed how unruly animals become before a storm? The champing at the bit, the strange restlessness, and sense of foreboding takes hold of animals as well as humans. The natives of India expect the weird and the unforeseen to happen before a monsoon, and it was on this theme that Louis Bromfield wrote his well-known book, *The Rains Came.*

If you want to find out whether your personality can weather a storm, try enduring a real one!

If you are undernourished, tired, fearful, and maladjusted, you'll huddle up in a corner, flinch at every flash of lightning, and feel sorry for yourself until the storm is over. Or your brain may be functioning so poorly that the lashing wind and roar of thunder make you panicky with fear.

If you go to your doctor on one of these days when the weather is against you, the complaints may fall from your lips faster than he can take them down: general discomfort, fatigue, headache, dizziness, nausea, faintness, and fast, labored breath.

In addition he might find that you have an increased pulse and blood pressure, that your rheumatism or arthritis is worsening, or that you are suffering from an asthma or sinus attack.

I explained some of this to Gil Bledsoe, who was suffering from a headache and hay fever attack one sultry afternoon.

"I know the weather is responsible for my hay fever," he said, "but it can't possibly account for my other symptoms."

"What are your other symptoms?" I asked.

"Nearly everything you can think of," he said. "I'm mentally depressed, tense, and irritable. I have a big business deal coming up, and not a bit of confidence in my ability to handle it."

I opened the blinds to Gil's picture window and looked out. "See those dark, threatening clouds out there?" I asked. "Well, they tell us that the barometer is falling. And judging from the way you describe your feelings, it's falling rather rapidly."

"Sure, sure," said Gil. "But how can this falling barometer affect me?"

"You may know," I said, "that the normal atmospheric pressure, owing to the weight of the earth's atmosphere, is 14.7 pounds per square inch at sea level."

"No, I didn't know that," said Gil.

"When atmospheric pressure drops below normal," I explained, "some of the air that's been forced into permeable places in the ground (such as interstices of loose soil, caves, fault crevices, and springs) then re-enters the lower atmosphere."

"So far, I'm following you," said Gil. "Then what happens?"

"Most soils," I said, "are slightly radioactive. They contain the naturally occurring minerals, particularly uranium and thorium, but also the more common compounds containing potassium, which emit radioactivity. These radioactive emissions which are forced out of the soil during the dropping atmospheric pressure create *ions,* or charged particles. The ionized air exhaled by the earth before a storm creates the discomfort that you feel."

"Well, what do you know!" he exclaimed. "Who found that out?"

"The first recorded discovery of the effect of these positive ions on a human being," I said, "occurred when an engineer, Nils Lindenblad, was working for RCA on radio research with a Van de Graaff generator. During some days, he had to expose himself to positive ionization, and on other days he was exposed to negative ions."

"What happened?" asked Gil. "Was there a difference in the way he felt?"

"Indeed there was," I said, "a distinct difference in the reaction of his personality to the positive and to the negative ions."

Lindenblad, usually calm and even-tempered, began acting like a dual personality. On some nights he was ebullient, joking, laughing, and frantically gay. On other nights, his car-pool companions noticed that he was morose, despondent, and critical— even asking them to stop talking.

"Lindenblad went to a doctor," I said, "to find the reason for his mood swings, but there was nothing physically wrong with him. Then he noticed that there was a startling correlation between his moods and whether the Van de Graaff generator was operating on a positive or negative polarity. He was manic, or happy, when he'd spent a day operating the generator on negative polarity. Following a day of positive polarity, he was depressive. By comparison, think of how you feel on the days when the barometric pressure goes up—the way you feel on a crisp, fall day!"

"Don't say that," Gil moaned. "I wish this were a crisp, fall day."

"You feel exhilarated on such a day," I said, "because the air containing positive ions is being forced back into the ground by the rising pressure. The cooler air, containing a greater number of negative ions, is showering those negative ions on you from above."

"I hate to be a skeptic," said Gil, "but I still don't believe it."

"Remember," I said, "that the cause of lightning is a heavy build-up of negative static electricity on the under side of clouds—which finally accumulates until it jumps to the positively charged surface of the earth. Now, doesn't this theory of lightning help to clarify the theory of the ions?"

But the analysis of the ions doesn't end there. These tiny electrical charges control many minute phenomena, right in our own bodies. It is generally agreed among many doctors that the mechanism of human sight occurs when images are communicated from the retina to the brain via the optic nerve by very low voltage electrical charges.

And according to Dr. Theodore T. Puck, of the University of Colorado Medical Center, viruses invade a human cell due to electrical charges. Dr. Puck says that normally both the virus and the cell are negatively charged. As long as this is the case, the charges repel each other and the virus cannot enter the cell. But if malnutrition or a traumatic experience influences the cell to have a positive charge, then, due to the electrical positive-negative attraction set up by the weakening of the cell, the virus enters to do its damage.

Dr. Puck's findings go a long way toward explaining why some people are more disease-resistant than others, as well as why we are more susceptible to virus in bad weather.

"Do you suppose," asked Gil, "that I'll always be a victim of such weather as this?"

"Soon we may be able to control our daily temperature curves," I said. "Today we can say definitely that ionized air has a physiological effect on us. Tomorrow—who knows?—we may be able to buy a little ionizer as easily as we can an air conditioner."

Much still remains to be learned about this phenomenon, even though for the past two hundred years biologists have known that electricity is connected with life. Every cell produces electricity. Every movement, even to the wink of an eye, discharges electricity. But we do know that only if you have a healthy, well-nourished body can you take the effects of severe weather changes without damage to your physical well-being as well as to your mental outlook.

"In weather like this," Gil said, "there ought to be something I could take to lessen my discomfort."

"You could take vitamin E," I said, "to lower your blood pressure under the present atmospheric conditions."

"How does vitamin E help my blood pressure?" he asked.

"To get enough oxygen out of the positively charged air," I said, "your heart has to beat faster, and your blood pressure rises. Vitamin E decreases the spasm in the smaller arteries, and improves the tone of the heart by decreasing its oxygen requirement."

Of the five factors of blood pressure—volume of blood, viscosity or thickness of the blood, the strength of the heartbeat, the elasticity of the vessel walls, and peripheral resistance—the one chiefly involved in blood pressure is peripheral resistance. Vitamin E lowers the resistance to the flow of blood by relaxing the terminal vessels (arterioles) which are in spasm.

"That certainly sounds worth trying," said Gil. "Any other suggestions to lessen my discomfort during a heat wave?"

"By understanding your body's cooling system," I said, "you realize that there is a way of eating that benefits you during the summer."

The body's main thermostat is the hypothalamus, a gland at the top of the spinal column. The hypothalamus is sensitive to the blood-sugar level as well as to the temperature surrounding the body. As the fuel foods affect the hypothalamus, it "tells" the blood vessels to enlarge. This allows more inside heat to rise to the skin surface. Under the influence of the hypothalamus, the skin becomes a radiator, transferring the extra heat from the body to the surrounding air.

"What's the next step?" he asked. "How do I keep this thermostat operating to cool me off?"

"By eating foods that will tend to keep your hypothalamus and your blood sugar at more constant levels," I said. "Use honey instead of sugar. Cut out the starches. Eat more of the high-protein foods: meat, fish, poultry, eggs, and low-fat cheeses."

Most bodies use protein during the summer to burn up surplus fats. The slower burning protein helps the body's cooling system by keeping the thermostat at a more constant level. It prunes off the fat, so the body has to work less to cool itself or to accomplish a given amount of activity.

Just like a thermostat, the sensitive hypothalamus should be maintained at a constant level for best operation. Starch and sugar affect the hypothalamus in much the same manner as paper burning in your furnace, flaring up swiftly, then immediately burning out. They cause your blood-sugar level to rise sharply, rapidly, then drop precipitously. Often the acute drops in the blood-sugar level produce a craving for more sugar, and when this craving is not satisfied (or when the blood-sugar level remains low), you experience such symptoms as weakness, tension, fearfulness, and confusion.

Hot, humid weather in summer is particularly hard on the heart. Heat decreases the body's efficiency and makes the heart work harder. During summer's heat, it has been found that the heartbeat increases by as much as 50 per cent.

"How about keeping my thermostat operating efficiently during all the seasons?" asked Gil.

"Protein is still the answer," I said. "And by keeping your hypothalamus operating well, you fortify your body for weather changes by protecting it from the traumatic experience that a severe weather change might cause."

"In other words," said Gil, "keep my body cells charged with negative ions."

"Yes," I said, "because in that way your cells can remain protected from viruses. They'll have the reserve stamina to resist diseases, as well as the sudden chilling or positive charges that fill the air."

"Weather forecasting is becoming more accurate," said Gil, "instead of the hit-or-miss affair it used to be. Now, thanks to the radio and TV, we generally know ahead of time when we're in for a siege of bad weather. I know I'm going to feel miserable, but, the thing is, I never knew what to do about it before."

"The more accurate the weather forecasting," I said, "the more accurate can be the diet forecasting. You can fortify your body for any predicted bad weather by the right choice of food. And in time, when the earth satellites can shake themselves free of the earth's atmosphere, they will be able to meter the changes in the sun's intensity. Then we'll have excellent new weather data, resulting in long-range weather forecasting."

"After the rough deal the weather has been giving me," Gil said, stifling a sneeze, "I'll take some of your long-range diet forecasting right now."

7

The Feminine Personality:
How To Eat for Beauty

E VERY woman has within her the potential of beauty.
The definitions of beauty are many, varied, and conflict-
ing. How *shall* we define it? As that nebulous thing which exists
only in the eye of the beholder? Or as something that our grandmothers maintained is only "skin-deep"?

The famous photographer and authority on beautiful women,
Erwin Blumenfeld, says, "A woman must have two things to be
beautiful. The first is personality. That is the only thing that
counts in life. You can't fake it . . . The other necessity for beauty
is enthusiasm. The capacity to fight with joy for something.
Women must be educated away from conformity, and into the
personal adventure."

Personality . . . enthusiasm . . . the personal adventure! These
are more than skin-deep. They come from within. From the glow
of health, that gives the freshness and bloom to a face. From the
wellspring of vitality which transforms each day, however
humdrum, into one that is interesting and adventurous.

The girl who sat before me was beautifully groomed and
expensively gowned, but the carefully applied make-up failed
to hide the dry, pallid skin, her look of fatigue, and the dark
circles under her eyes.

"I'm in desperate trouble," she told me. "I'm losing my looks—

growing old before my time—and nothing seems to help me!"

Fading beauty is a misfortune to many women, but to this girl it was a genuine tragedy. She was Lillian Collins, a well-known model whose very livelihood depended on her appearance and personality.

"You say nothing seems to help," I said. "What have you been trying?"

"Almost everything," she said, "that well-meaning friends have suggested, or that I've read about in *Vogue* and *Harper's Bazaar* —hormone and vitamin creams, royal jelly, moisturizers—even that new orchid-pollen extract from France that's supposed to be brimming with vitamins, minerals, protein, and amino acids."

"Then perhaps you also read," I said, "in a recent issue of *Vogue* this statement: 'We believe that there is a way, comfortably and attractively, this side of food faddism, *to eat your way to beauty*. We think that diet may be, in some cases, the *only* way to correct certain beauty flaws.'"

"No," Miss Collins said, "I'm afraid I didn't. And I must admit that I'm rather surprised."

"It's an encouraging viewpoint," I went on, "in a magazine dedicated to beauty, high fashion, and cosmetic consciousness. They went on to say that an astonishing number of beauty flaws —the look of fatigue, lackluster hair, rough skin, and unclear eyes, possibly even puffiness under the eyes and puffiness of the ankles—*may be nutritional in source*. 'And where nutrition is at fault,' they concluded, 'the repair job, if it's to be the real thing, should be via food.' Of course all nutritionists have known this for years, but unfortunately you women won't listen to us as readily as you will to a beauty editor."

"I'll listen now," she said. "My whole future is at stake. My work has fallen off, and it's easy to see why. Every time I look in the mirror I see a new line that refuses to be massaged away— even these whistle lines around my lips! I'm not old enough for these. I don't know why I have them all of a sudden. They're very faint now, and make-up almost hides them, but they'll get deeper and deeper, lipstick will smear in them, and the camera will reveal them. You don't know how brutal the camera can be!"

"The whistle lines," I said, "are one of the symptoms of a riboflavin deficiency. That, and rough, chapped, or flaking lips, a purplish tongue, and an upper lip that grows smaller by degrees until in some cases it seems almost to disappear, if the deficiency is of long standing."

"Is it possible," she asked, "that a vitamin deficiency can do all that to my looks?"

"All that," I replied, "and much more. The symptoms of a vitamin-C deficiency are those typical of old age. If you don't eat enough citrus fruits, tomatoes, or raw cabbage, you can expect wrinkles, loss of elasticity of the skin, loss of teeth, and brittle bones. And there's a B vitamin so important to youthful appearance that it's been called the 'anti-gray-hair' factor."

"I've heard of that one," Lillian said. "That's called pantothenic acid, isn't it?"

"That's right," I said. "And prematurely gray hair is only one of the symptoms of a pantothenic acid deficiency. Others are painful, aching feet, eczema, neuritis, inflammation of the intestines and the stomach, extreme fatigue, and the inability to think clearly. The richest food sources of pantothenic acid are: liver, dried yeast, kidney, unsulfured molasses, egg yolk, soybeans, peanuts, raw wheat germ, and dried peas and beans."

"I never eat any of those," she admitted. "So I must have a deficiency."

"I'm afraid," I said, "that yours is more than just one deficiency. You should eat a varied diet, high in protein, vitamins, and minerals, including the foods just mentioned. And supplement this diet with a high-potency B-complex product containing pantothenic acid. The B-complex vitamins taken in concert can do more for your body than the same vitamins taken singly."

From many case histories, it seems that pantothenic acid in adequate amounts can help to prolong youthfulness. Modern science believes that protein and the B vitamins delay aging, and meat and eggs are good sources of both.

"Your daily menu can be your secret formula for feeling young," Roberta Hershey, nutrition specialist at Michigan State University, tells her students. "And seven of the key letters in your formula are p-r-o-t-e-i-n."

Protein makes up a large part of every one of the billions of cells in your body. Each day some cells die and have to be replaced. *If no protein is available to replace worn-out body cells, body tissue breaks down and aging takes place.* Protein contributes to the health and beauty of your hair, skin, and nails. It firms your muscles, aids in steadying your nerves, and, with vitamin C and iron, enables your blood cells to get their supply of oxygen. Protein is needed for the building and upkeep of every part of your body.

"Then are a bad skin, premature aging, and wrinkles telltale signs of a nutritional deficiency?" asked Lillian.

"When there's an inadequate protein intake," I said, "you age fast, because you can't replace the cells that die. Your body does everything in its power to keep the vital organs functioning, so the cells that go first are the muscular cells that keep your skin smooth and firm. If more women realized this, perhaps they would eat *one or more protein foods at each meal.* But instead, most of you eat protein only once a day, and fall alarmingly short of even your minimum requirements."

"I can't eat protein every meal," she said, "because I have to diet to keep slim."

"You're making the mistake that most dieters make," I said. "In trying to cut calories, you cut out the foods that are vital to life itself."

On a high-protein diet you can eat full meals, yet never have to worry about putting on weight, for protein burns up your fat and in the process gives you specific dynamic energy. You invest the capital of a good diet, and your body returns the dividends of vitality and beauty.

"Those dividends interest me," she said. "Tell me how to go about getting them."

I told Lillian to be sure to get *at least* 80 grams of protein a day—and the calorie count for proteins is lower than for sugars, fats, and starches—by including the following foods in her daily diet:

Meats: two large servings every day, preferably broiled, or roasted. (Never fried, nor should it be served with gravies.)

Eggs: At least one a day, poached or boiled.

Vegetables: Tomatoes and all leafy, green, and yellow vegetables, without butter or cream sauce. Lemon juice for seasoning.

Fruit: All fresh fruits, melons, and berries, with no cream or sugar.

Bread: Only whole-grain breads and cereals, and these in moderation.

Beverages: Fortify diet with powdered skim milk (one cup of powdered skim milk contains 43 grams of protein); or to satisfy between-meal hunger, drink a glass of buttermilk; or a cup of hot skim milk with a spoonful of honey stirred into it; or hot herbal tea with honey and lemon.

Desserts: Junket or baked custard made with skim milk, cheese, or fresh fruit. Frozen fruit may be eaten when fresh is not obtainable, or occasionally canned fruits, but avoid those packed in heavy syrup.

"I've never eaten that much in one day," Lillian said. "Of course I do eat salads, and I drink orange juice every day— usually the frozen kind."

"Then you are receiving, at the most, only about 30 milligrams of vitamin C," I said, "and that's not enough. You should have at least 250 milligrams daily."

The amount of vitamin C that you receive from citrus fruits depends upon the freshness of your source. Some loss of this perishable vitamin may occur within five minutes after an orange or grapefruit is cut, and losses of 90 per cent may occur within an hour. Yet there are still many housewives who, to save time in the early morning, squeeze a pitcher of orange juice the night before and leave it on ice for the family breakfast!

"I used to squeeze oranges the night before," Lillian said, "when I'd have an early appointment. But of course I didn't know that vitamin C was so perishable. Wouldn't it be better to take it just as a supplement?"

"Not *just* as a supplement," I said, "but in addition to the diet I've suggested for you. I certainly recommend a good vitamin-mineral food supplement containing vitamin C as well as the B vitamins, if you're anxious to prevent premature aging."

Dr. Walter H. Baker, of Columbia University, has said that many of the signs of aging are in reality the signs of scurvy—the disease that follows a prolonged lack of vitamin C.

"What about the minerals part of the supplement?" she asked. "What do they do for me?"

"The mineral story," I said, "is almost as fascinating as a woman."

Magnesium (which is found in beets, corn, cucumbers, onions, apples, berries, peaches, bananas, and pears) improves skin tone. Phosphorus (found in root vegetables, lentils, citrus fruits, lettuce, watercress, egg yolk, fish, lean meats, cheese, fowl, buttermilk, steel-cut oats, and almonds, to name a few) combines with magnesium and calcium to make strong teeth.

That most vital mineral, calcium, is usually the one most deficient in the diet of the average woman. That's one reason so many women suffer from tension and migraines, insomnia, and the inability to relax. Since the amount of calcium in a woman's blood often parallels the activity of her ovaries, she may suffer menstrual cramps at the onset of menstruation, due to the decrease of blood calcium.

"I don't want to be one of those cling-to-youth women," she said, "but in my business I simply have to look my best. As I mature, I want to do it gracefully—and as beautifully as possible. Lots of models make the transition from glamour girls to poised and charming matrons, and keep right on working. Why should I be an exception, and suddenly start looking like an old hag?"

"There's absolutely no need for it," I said, "if you keep your body in a state of well-being with sound nutrition and healthful activity."

Face your personal adventure of maturity with an eager, inquiring mind and a heart filled with enthusiasm and love for something or somebody. Thirty years ago Janet Gaynor became famous for her youthful innocence as Diane in the motion picture *Seventh Heaven*. Recently, resuming her career to star in a picture as Pat Boone's mother, she said, "There is no point in making yourself unhappy about departing youth when there is so much to replace it."

"She can afford to say that," Lillian said, "because she's still young-looking, beautiful, and completely charming . . . besides being happily married to Adrian, who designs those stunning clothes for her!"

"More than anything else," I said, "Miss Gaynor's physical well-being and unbounded interest in life have contributed to her youthful appearance and outlook."

When she began to paint, a whole new world opened up to her. As she and her husband traveled, they discovered adventures awaiting them in every port. She's always enjoyed good food, so she found excitement in trying the exotic dishes and the tropical fruits (rich in vitamins and minerals) on their South American plantation, where they live part of each year.

Miss Gaynor says that you needn't travel far away to find new interests. "You can create new interests anywhere," she tells us, "if there is sufficient enthusiasm and eagerness to learn. This is the essence of youth. And anyone who keeps a youthful point of view will be young in spirit and heart."

"Well," Lillian said, "I think it's about time I followed your advice. I've tried almost everything the beauty salons have to offer."

"From now on," I said, "spend your money on more meat, eggs, cheese, fresh fruits and vegetables, *and* vitamin-mineral food supplements. If you want genuine results, take your protein, vitamins, and minerals the only way that they actually benefit you—and that's by eating them, not rubbing them on."

Now, please understand that I'm all in favor of anything that increases a woman's attractiveness, builds up her morale, or makes her happier. I simply prefer the legitimate, healthful, and less expensive ways of doing it.

I enjoy seeing a woman who has applied powder, lipstick, and eye make-up with subtle artistry. But I deplore it if make-up is used to conceal a bad skin rather than to enhance a good one.

Like most men, I dislike lipstick or powder smeared on so thickly that it rubs off on the masculine sleeve—or lips, as the case may be! Make-up defeats itself if it's a barrier between a girl and romance. Let it be soft and inviting, with a suggestion of the possibility of love.

Time magazine had this to say recently about inner beauty: "To their credit, more and more women are realizing that beauty is more than skin-deep. *They want healthy, well-formed bodies and new personalities* to go with their made-up faces."

8

How Much of Your Personality Is a Hidden Iceberg?

"YOU knew about my promotion?" Jay Curtis asked me, when we met unexpectedly at a club luncheon.

"Yes, I heard about it," I said. "Congratulations!"

His smile was broad and friendly, but his eyes held a curious look of uncertainty. "I'm not so sure," he said, "that they're in order. I think you know that I wanted this job of sales manager for a long time. I worked like the devil to get it. But now that I have it—well, to coin a cliché, I feel like a square peg in a round hole."

"What's the matter?" I asked. "You certainly look like a man who's happy and successful in his work."

"Maybe I look it," he said, "but I sure don't feel it."

"On the surface," I said, "your personality appears to be that of a sales manager. The go-getter type—harried, a marionette of tensions, but aggressive, bold, and confident. Yet because personalities are like icebergs, the nine-tenths of you that lies submerged might be protesting against your being that type of personality."

"That's just it," Jay said. "Outwardly I'm aggressive because I have to be. While inside I'm quaking—a regular shrinking-violet type. Go ahead and laugh if you like, but it's true."

"Your personality really *is* in conflict," I said.

"So much so, that I'm going to have to change it to make a success of my job. And that isn't going to be easy, is it?" he asked.

"No, it isn't," I replied. "To change your personality, you must first change your habits. Your personality is bound up in a series of habits—the way you live, what you eat, your attitudes toward life, and your pattern of thought."

"It'll be a full-time project," Jay said, "to change all of those."

"A psychologist would tell you," I said, "that your personality can be changed only as the interrelated systems of habits and attitudes encompassing your personality are changed."

"Those guys are always so technical," he said. "You give it to me straight, without any fancy rhetoric."

"You must learn to understand that part of your personality which is submerged," I said, "the iceberg that lies beneath the water."

"That's the one that threatens my job," he said, "and is trying to wreck the course I've charted through life."

"Just how do you think your submerged personality threatens you?" I asked.

"It makes me think I'm not able to put over a deal," Jay said. "I get off to a good start, then I lose steam right in the middle of it. I get scared and think I can't do it. Just like the time when I was a little boy and almost won a swimming race. I started out with a bang, and was leading the race, but I'd rushed away from home without eating breakfast—and just a few yards from the finish, I didn't have the strength to swim any more. I lost the race."

"Do you still rush away from home without eating breakfast?" I asked.

"Certainly not!" said Jay. "That taught me a lesson."

"I'm very glad to hear it," I said. "What do you eat?"

"I always have two or three cups of coffee to get me going," he said, "and usually a sweet roll or doughnut."

"Then you'll keep right on losing steam before noon," I said, "and it won't be from an unfounded fear or anxiety on your part.

It'll be because you still haven't learned your lesson well enough to know what constitutes a good breakfast. If you don't eat the right type of breakfast, your blood sugar can fall from 92 to 58 mg. of glucose per 100 cc. within a few hours."

"Is that bad?" asked Jay.

"I'll tell you how bad it is," I said. "You can't even move or think without adequate glucose in your blood. If you're healthy, the amount of sugar in your blood should fluctuate only between 80 and 140 mg. per 100 cc. of blood per hour. Chronic partial sugar starvation of your brain cells can fog your thinking, dull your moral sense, and distort your normally realistic conception of your relationship to the world. It's been proved that the brain waves of persons with low blood sugar are abnormal. And scientists are now proving that there's a definite correlation between low blood sugar and certain types of insanity."

"Maybe," said Jay, "I should have *my* brain waves examined."

"It's a very serious matter," I said. "If your blood sugar fluctuates beyond the margin of safety, it results in coma and death."

"If that's the reason that I cool off so quickly, after starting out like a ball of fire, what can I do about it?" Jay asked.

"You can change your eating habits so you'll be getting the proper foods at the time when they'll do you the most good," I said. "A good breakfast is the most essential meal of the day, because you have to accomplish a lot of work on it."

"And I gather," he said, "that you disapprove of sweet rolls and doughnuts."

"*Disapprove* is too mild a word," I said. "They're an insult to your stomach. You should eat a breakfast that gives you at least one, and preferably two, of the high-quality and complete proteins found in meat, eggs, fish, poultry, or cheese."

"Meat and eggs *both?*" asked Jay, as though he never heard of such a thing. "On weekdays as well as Sundays?"

"Don't you need just as much food to put across your business deals on weekdays as you do to loaf on Sundays?" I asked.

"You don't know me," said Jay. "I really *work* at loafing. And I do eat meat for dinner, and sometimes for lunch."

"You need protein every meal—three times a day—if your body is to maintain the even blood-sugar level which will enable you to perform with your energy potential," I said.

Two scientists, Dr. R. M. Leverton and Dr. M. R. Gram, found in experiments that subjects who received plenty of high-quality protein divided among three daily meals were in positive nitrogen balance, while those who received the same amount at only two of the meals were in negative balance. The total daily intake of protein for all of the subjects in the experiment was the same.

"Why is it so essential to have a positive nitrogen balance?" he asked.

"So you can be a healthy, efficient personality, able to do your best on the job," I answered. "When you lose your positive nitrogen balance, premature aging steps in. Your cells die off too fast without being replaced, and your body isn't able to carry on all of life's processes."

"If my body gets so much protein from time to time," he said, "I still don't see why it matters when I eat it."

Dr. E. Geiger, Dr. P. R. Cannon, and other scientists have demonstrated that if there is an interval longer than one hour between the time you eat an incomplete protein (one without all the amino acids) and another protein which supplies the missing amino acids of the first, there is failure of tissue synthesis. All of the essential amino acids should be provided simultaneously and in desirable proportions if they are to be efficiently utilized.

"So protein would keep me going full steam ahead," asked Jay, "when my coffee and doughnut won't?"

"Indeed it would," I said. "Protein has Specific Dynamic Action, because it maintains a constant blood-sugar level for at least five hours while it's being digested. On a breakfast of meat and eggs, you find yourself with the same pep at noon that you had when you started out early in the morning. Conversely, your 'breakfast' of doughnuts and coffee causes your blood-sugar level to rise unduly at eight o'clock and to slump to rock bottom by ten— about the time you say you run out of steam in the middle of a deal."

"Then that explains why I'm always hungry just about an hour after I've eaten," Jay said. "But there's another thing that bothers me about this job. It makes me tense."

"You should get rid of that false idea," I said. "Your job doesn't make you too tense. You're too tense on your job."

"But it's pretty rough going sometimes," he insisted. "The work wears me out and I'm always tired."

"It's not because you overwork," I said. "You're tired because you're too tense. Challenging events and fear that you won't be able to put over your deal promote your states of tension. To meet each situation, you put your whole organism in a state of hyperactivity."

"I'm going to try eating enough protein," Jay said, "starting with breakfast, to give me that Specific Dynamic Energy you speak of. Then maybe I'll lose my fear of these interviews, and the tension that I suffer during them."

"You could also prepare your body to handle these challenges that promote your tension," I said.

Tension is a shortening of muscle fibers, which has three phases. The physical shortening is one phase, and it is chemical. This phase consumes oxygen and results in the breaking down of complex phosphate compounds. But if you look at it from the viewpoint that the muscles have shortened because they have received an electrical impulse from the brain through your nerve synapse junction, the process may be considered electrical, or what is called "action potential." In this total circuit in the organism, there is the "effort circuit." If poor nerves inhibit the message from your brain, it isn't transmitted to the muscle making the effort. It may be cross-circuited and transmitted to many muscles, which results in unnecessary thrashing about, as in cases of panic. Such an extreme state of tension cannot result in any productive activity on your part.

"Then the thing for me to do," Jay said, "is to control my tensions so they result in productive activity, instead of just much ado about nothing."

"Yes," I said, "if you want to become the successful sales-manager type of personality, you must guide your tensions into the productive activity of putting your article across and getting your prospects to buy it. All other tension is wasted effort."

"I agree with you," Jay said. "But I still don't know how to control my tensions."

"First, you have to control your brain," I said, "so that it can accomplish straight thinking. Next, you must control your nerves so they respond to specific signals rather than to the din of sub-way trains, traffic, the clatter of dishes, or the jangling of the telephone. And third, you must send out your effort signals directly to the muscle which you specifically want to obey them."

"If I could do that," Jay said, "I could stop spinning my wheels and get somewhere. Because I'd be controlling most of that part of my unconscious—my submerged personality—wouldn't I?"

"Exactly," I said. "So many people are prey to the tensions caused by that hidden part of the mind which is a seething mass of drives, motives, experiences, observations, and conflicts. They let the submerged part of their personality control their lives."

"But how can I control these conflicts in the hidden iceberg part of my personality?"

"By controlling your personality with the part of the iceberg that's in full view—your conscious," I said. "A diet that will keep your mind and body vibrant with healthful energy is helpful. And that brings us back to our old friend, protein."

A protein deficiency—which may lead to a vitamin and mineral deficiency as well—manifests itself chiefly in a sense of habitual fatigue, the more extreme deficiencies leading to anemia, edema, atrophy of muscles and other tissues. Scientists have found that adult humans on a high-protein diet absorbed 15 per cent of their dietary calcium, while those on a low-protein diet absorbed less than 5 per cent of the calcium received in their foods.

"How does calcium get into this battle to control tensions?" Jay asked.

"It belongs there," I said, "because calcium is extremely important for the health of your nerve cells. The nerve cells of the aged are generally shrunken in outline, the nuclei appear faded, the granules are clumped together, and the connective tissue increases moderately in volume. Your nerve cells are your longest-lived cells, but if you haven't enough calcium, these cells begin to degenerate when you're much younger. And degenerated nerve cells aren't able to send out the direct impulses that help you control your tensions."

"So I need protein and calcium," Jay said. "Anything else?"

"Lecithin—along with all the vitamins and minerals," I replied. "Especially the B vitamins, which are essential in the feeding of your nerve cells and your brain.

"Without sufficient thiamine, your body can't convert the food you eat into nourishment for your brain. If your brain is starved, first you lose your equilibrium and feel dizzy, then you lose contact with reality and become neurotic, and finally, psychotic. Lack of glutamic acid in the brain can result in epilepsy, and the brain, lacking the enzyme cholinesterase in certain areas of the cortex, becomes maze-dull in animals, or lacking in intelligence."

"I don't like the sound of those symptoms," Jay said. "I'll have to remember to provide my brain with plenty of good, nourishing protein snacks so it won't get any duller than it is. I didn't know it could be starved."

With the exception of the brain and the nerve cells, man's body is a chemical machine which reproduces itself every few months. What we are just learning is that we can control the efficiency of man with the amount and kind of raw materials that we give this chemical machine to operate on. We are learning that by keeping the body in a positive nitrogen balance, with sufficient proteins, lecithin, vitamins, and minerals at the proper time, we can expect vibrant health, efficient control over our tensions and energies, and the personality that can withstand emotional and physical stress and disease.

"Until we know more, we had best control the submerged portion of our personality with what knowledge we have," I added.

"But even if I do feed my unconscious properly," Jay said, "I can't expect to banish it. I'm afraid it's here to stay."

"You can build up a strong enough personality to withstand its challenges," I said. "You can face your unconscious and become aware of its creative, as well as its frustrating potentials. The strong body can overcome these hidden conflicts before they exert their pathological, inhibiting hold on will power and intellect."

"I'd like to be able to make my personality fit me," Jay said, "instead of hindering me, as mine has been doing."

"You've built up your personality, mentally, physically, and emotionally, over the years, Jay. It's true that you received the bare outlines of your personality structure—your temperament and your I. Q.—through inheritance, but you've filled in your outline with your daily living and eating habits."

Both physical stature *and* personality depend on diet—as an example, look at the Japanese and the taller, sturdier Nisei. While an individual personality might be a continuum, following the outlines of heredity, each personality develops continually from infancy until death.

"If that's the case," Jay said, "I should be able to adjust my personality to any environment—even my job."

"The adjustment of his personality to his environment has been done by man since the beginning of time," I said. "Your personality strives to solve the twofold problem of human living. Your body strives to meet your physical needs, and your mind strives to manage the demands of social reality. If, through an improper diet, the second problem is ignored, you certainly will find it difficult to solve the other.

"The chemical imbalance from poor and deficient meals upsets your body's physical equilibrium, and you become physically ill—then your mental homeostasis (balance) becomes easily upset by mismanaged emotions. It's next to impossible for the ill or undernourished to manage the demands of social reality."

"When I learn to control that hidden iceberg part of my personality," Jay said, "and can make it work *for* me instead of against me, maybe I'll stop feeling like that square peg in the round hole. Maybe I'll fit."

"I have no doubt of it," I said. "Perhaps you'll find, as I have, a lot of wisdom in these words of Bertrand Russell:

> I find men in our dangerous age who seem to be in love with misery and death . . . They think that hope is irrational and that, in sitting down to lazy despair, they are merely facing facts . . . To preserve hope in our world makes calls upon our intelligence and our energy. *In those who despair, it is very frequently energy that is lacking.*

9

Fatigue Is a Personality Thief

"I'VE spent more money than I can afford on tonics and cure-alls," Eve Sinclair said. "But I'm still so tired that I can hardly get through a day's work."

That tired feeling! The number of persons who suffer from it is overwhelming. It's an all-too-common complaint from both men and women, rich or poor, in every walk of life. So common, in fact, that last year Americans spent over four hundred million dollars trying to alleviate it and muster the necessary energy to meet the demands of life.

Housewives, executives, schoolteachers, stenographers, bankers —no one is immune. What's the reason for it? Is it because most of us live and work at a frantic, frustrating pace, which produces emotional and psychological upsets that further deplete our energies?

Although we can blame the Atomic Age for many of our ills, the fatigue symptoms that we suffer today were not unknown to our ancestors. In the seventeenth century, the English concocted a robust (if unappetizing!) potion of iron filings steeped in Rhenish wine for the weak and ailing.

And even before that, the Hindus, like the Greeks (who drank water in which swords had been rusted), had a remedy for fatigue: powdered iron, oil, whey, and herbs. In our not-so-ancient days, there was the plight of Elizabeth Barrett, who was forced to drink porter, which she loathed, for the sake of her health. But when romance, in the person of Robert Browning, gave her a new interest in life and love, she regained her appetite, her energy was renewed, and her health improved.

"I don't like the word *cure-all*," I told Eve. "Money spent on a good vitamin-mineral food supplement is different—it's an investment in health, and I heartily endorse it. Yet even with that, you can't neglect eating the foods that are essential for health and energy. These include the vitamin- and mineral-rich fresh fruits and vegetables, and the high-protein foods which are generally those rich in iron as well. And the necessity for iron to combat fatigue seems to be one thing that's agreed on, from the ancients on down—although their methods of putting iron into the diet were varied and dubious."

"I've been trying anything and everything," Eve said, "because I'm worried. My personality has deteriorated, and I've slowed down, both mentally and physically. The most inexperienced girls in my office can work rings around me now. I *know* there's something wrong with me, but my doctor can't find what it is."

Again the plea, "What's wrong with me?" that I hear constantly. Not really sick, yet far from well. Tired out from tasks that should be taken in stride, tense and irritable—a victim of chronic fatigue.

"Even a mild form of nutritional deficiency," I said, "can impair your personality, decrease your energy, and slow down your productivity. If your doctor has ruled out any serious physical disorder, the next thing to do is to look at your diet. Is it nutritionally sound or is it skimpy?"

"Well," Eve said, "by your standards it may seem skimpy. But it's the way nearly every working girl I know eats. I usually have orange juice and coffee for breakfast, a sandwich or salad for lunch—but I do eat a big dinner—when I'm not too rushed or too tired."

"Then it's not surprising that you're weak, tired, and lacking in energy during the day," I said. "And instead of being pepped up by your big dinner, you probably still feel tired, and sluggish and drowsy as well."

"Yes, I do," she said. "I haven't been able to understand that. Just when I could relax and enjoy the evening hours, I'm absolutely too dopey to do anything."

"There's a very good reason for it," I said. "A large meal robs you of energy by taking the blood sugar from your brain and muscles—which accounts for your lassitude and drowsiness—sending it into the stomach and intestines, where your energy is utilized to digest all that food. This naturally leaves you feeling dull, and as you said, dopey. You'd be in far better health and spirits if you ate three medium-sized, well-balanced meals a day, starting with the most important one of all, breakfast. And by the way, what do you have on your coffee breaks?"

"Why, coffee, of course," she said. "Or sometimes a Coke. I have to have a stimulant to give me a lift, even though it never seems to last me until I get back to work."

"You're a victim of your own bad eating habits. And you won't get over your chronic fatigue until you change them. Your breakfast should provide enough nourishment to see you halfway through your day's work without a letdown. Start with a whole orange—not just the juice!—or a half grapefruit to step up your metabolism. Then have eggs and meat or a cheese omelet for that all-important protein, and a whole-grain seed cereal with nonfat milk at least occasionally.

"Instead of coffee or Coke on your break," I said, "have fresh fruit or buttermilk. Or, for quick energy, drink a cup of hot water with honey in it. A good between-meal nibble that you could keep in your desk are ready-to-eat sunflower seeds. They're an excellent source of protein, iron, and vitamins A and D and the B vitamins, especially thiamine.

"And, since exercise is vital to energy, you might take part of your break for a brisk, five-minute walk. A relaxed, cheerful attitude helps combat fatigue, for there's an amazing chemical link between nervous tension and energy; when you're worried, depressed, tense, or anxious, it reduces the amount of glucose absorbed into the bloodstream."

Are you bored with your work? If so, you can expect to become physically fatigued as well as mentally lethargic, and the RAS may be to blame for it, according to experiments made by the University of California at Los Angeles.

And what is this rascal, RAS, that it can do that to us?

The RAS is the Reticular Activating System, which screens stimuli to the brain. Its task is to alert the mind when necessary and to keep out useless messages. But when you're bored with your job and under excessively monotonous conditions, such as a dull, daily routine—washing dishes, typing letters, adding columns of figures, talking to people who bore you, or whatever!— it is believed that the RAS *keeps your brain only half awake, and some of the brain's messages needed to mobilize the body's energy are lost.*

"No matter how exhausted I am," Eve said, "or how sleepy I feel before I get into bed, I'm still troubled with insomnia."

"Then your body must not be able to co-ordinate its fatigue into a whole that produces sleep," I said. "If nervous tension isn't erased by increased circulation of the blood, activated glands, and good food, it produces a toxin which can deplete the nervous system."

"I suppose it's nervous fatigue, all right," she said. "I lie awake half the night and think of all my problems."

"When your mind becomes so active unconsciously that it's impossible to switch it off," I said, "you're incurring a debt of sleep that accumulates at compound interest. And the more frequently you fail to get your normal rest, the harder it will be for you to return to a state of nervous solvency."

"I tried sleeping pills," she said, "but they gave me a bad hangover effect the next morning, and I could hardly get up in time to go to work."

"*Hangover* is a well-chosen word," I said, "because sleeping pills may give you one. Their excessive use often results in a mild, continuous sort of jag, with its attendant loss of memory, thick or stumbling speech, and inability to concentrate."

"All of those effects," Eve asked, "from such harmless-looking little pills?"

"They're not so harmless!" I replied. "And if you have any left, get rid of them! The only way that you'll be able to find real sleep is by eliminating the causes of your nervous fatigue. The best way to do that is through relaxation and a proper diet to correct your deficiencies. A mineral deficiency, in particular, is a ruthless sleep destroyer."

"Do you mean," Eve asked, "that there are foods which promote sleep?"

"Two natural sleep inducers are calcium and lactic acid," I said. "Lactic acid is produced by your muscles when they're exercised sufficiently. Did you ever know a laborer, farmer, or lumberjack who suffered from insomnia?"

"I never knew any farmers, laborers, or lumberjacks," she said. "But I used to know a swimming champion. One time when there was no ocean, channel, lake, or swimming pool handy, he took me to the opera—but he slept right through it, and even snored!"

"You see?" I said. "Fresh air and exercise released calcium and lactic acid into his bloodstream. When the calcium reached the sleep center of his brain, his conscious mind ceased to send out nerve impulses to his muscles. Then sleep was inevitable—and I hope you forgave the poor fellow!"

"I'm afraid I envied his ability to go to sleep so easily," she said, "at the opera, or any place. But even if exercise would make me drowsy, I can't go around flexing my muscles and thumping my chest the way he did."

"Of course not," I said. "But your bloodstream absolutely has to have enough calcium and lactic acid before your brain's sleep center can produce inactivity of the conscious mind and sleepiness. Calcium is in your bloodstream when you eat nutritious, well-balanced meals. And if you don't get enough exercise to produce lactic acid, then you must eat foods that contain this lullaby aid."

"I remember that you get calcium in milk," Eve said. "But what foods contain lactic acid?"

"Buttermilk and yogurt are rich in both of them," I said, "and you can also indirectly create these two substances in your blood by using plenty of nonfattening dried skim milk."

The bad effects of loss of sleep are hard to measure, as they may be slow in catching up with you. First, a loss of ambition and zest for living, a weariness and lassitude that won't go away, and soon you notice that you catch cold more easily. As your resistance becomes lower, a more serious disease which you might have escaped, may threaten you. You become tense and irritable, your work slows down, and your mind is less alert. Your fatigue becomes chronic, your personality diminishes or changes from radiant to dull. Tension and anxiety are your most constant companions.

"Perhaps there are anxiety-causing factors somewhere in your life or job that you're afraid to face," I went on, "so you lie in bed and worry about them in that twilight state between sleeping and waking. If your problems can't be eliminated, at least you can build up your health so you're able to face them during your waking hours, instead of worrying about them at night."

Dr. Edmund Jacobson, Director of the Laboratory for Clinical Physiology, Chicago, has this to say about insomnia:

> In all matters, by day or night, try to keep yourself as completely relaxed as possible . . . wrestling with the day's problems is a sure road to sleeplessness. Let *everything* go for the morrow. It is effort that keeps you awake. If by careful preparation during the day you can learn to sacrifice all effort—even the effort to sleep— you will find that the blessing of relaxed and refreshing rest is yours.

In restful sleep (the kind that restores and refreshes your body and mind), heart action and breathing are slowed down considerably. Your body temperature drops to subnormal levels, the muscles and the walls of your blood vessels relax, which reduces blood pressure and drains your brain of its blood.

Sleep is one of the preventives against aging too fast. The Russian scientist Professor S. Braines says that lack of sleep is the greatest single cause of premature old age. Further, it causes muscle tone to diminish, hair to fall out, and sexual powers to disappear long before the calendar years say they should.

And, since disturbed sleep cannot insure restorative processes of the body tissues, insomnia leads to far-reaching disturbances in the physiological processes. An animal can endure hunger for as long as thirty days, but ten days without sleep causes death.

Taking good care of your body by giving it the necessary nutrients is a far better fatigue chaser and sleep inducer than sheep rotaters, metronomic lullers, sleep shades, or relaxing records.

A good vitamin-mineral food supplement rounds out a well-balanced diet. It provides ample quantities of the B-complex vitamins to nourish nerves. Vitamin B_1 (thiamine) specifically nourishes the nerve cells, and a lack of it is one of the most prevalent causes of chronic fatigue. If your diet doesn't include the whole grains, ample portions of beef, lamb, or the organ meats —liver, heart, or kidney—it is quite likely to be deficient in thiamine. And vitamin C plays a big part in controlling the effects of brain fag by contributing to the health of the blood vessels of the brain and body.

"It sounds as though there's hardly a vitamin or mineral that I *don't* need," Eve said.

"You must have them all," I said, "to provide health for your body, nerves, and brain, and the energy necessary for the mere business of living. Recent research on energy consumption has uncovered some figures that you'd hardly believe. A Columbia University report says that just standing increases our energy consumption by 18 per cent, and bad posture wastes up to twice as much energy."

Involuntarily, Eve straightened the discouraged slump of her shoulders, and said defensively, "Most of the time I'm simply too tired to hold myself erect, although I do know the value of good posture."

"And your poor posture leads to still further fatigue," I said. "Next to three well-balanced meals a day high in proteins, vitamins, and minerals, one of the secrets of a tireless, nerve-free body and mind lies in deep, natural breathing. And you'll find that your weary slump or slouch will disappear when you're filling your lungs to capacity."

Nervous tension diminishes as physical fatigue is lessened. Muscle tissues are automatically supplied with the increased oxygen that is necessary for sustained physical vitality. Practice deep breathing every morning and every night before retiring—it helps relax you for sleep, too. But don't just heave your chest up and down and think you're doing it correctly—the only movement that should occur is the expansion and contraction of your lower ribs. If you place your hands on your rib cage you can feel whether or not the expansion and contraction are occurring in the right place, and slowly, rhythmically, instead of jerkily.

The types of fatigue are many and varied. Some respond immediately to simple measures, while others need more prolonged and intensive treatment, but not one can fail to benefit from improved eating habits.

First on the list of fatigue causes I would place peristaltic fatigue, due to incorrect diet. Others, although not necessarily in the given order, are a run-down state still existing in those recovering from illness; auditory fatigue caused by noise; optical fatigue due to over-use of the eyes; unhappiness in marriage or work (which can lead to disuse of practically all the systems of the body, setting a pernicious cycle in motion, causing more fatigue); excessive smoking or drinking; and general physical fatigue caused by hard work or loss of sleep. The easiest fatigue of all to overcome, this last is usually remedied by a good night's sleep and rest.

"I'd like to regain a zest for life and the interests I used to have," Eve said. "I've become so dull and uninteresting that I hate to be around people, yet I want and need companionship. It's not the desire to have friends that's lacking—I'm just too tired to make the effort."

"Since vitality is something that dancers must have in abundance, I'd like to tell you what Cyd Charisse says about it. 'When I am dancing I go into training,' she said recently in an interview. 'I eat a good strong breakfast. *You have so much more energy if you start your day well fortified.*' Of course I've been telling everybody that for a long time, but people are more impressed when a beautiful girl sets an example."

"Indeed they are," Eve said. "I perked up my ears and listened when you mentioned Cyd Charisse. Whatever it is that makes her so beautiful and gives her such a vibrant personality, I'd like to know about it, and see if it would work for me."

"Then listen to what she has for breakfast," I said, "and let it be an example for you! 'I like hot cereal, two eggs, fruit juice with gelatin in it,' Miss Charisse says. More protein, you'll notice! 'Sometimes I have a ground-beef patty. During the day when I have a strenuous rehearsal, I may take a teaspoon of honey in a glass of juice for quick energy.'"

"Why, that's just about the same thing you've been telling me," Eve said.

"I know," I said, "but Miss Charisse is prettier than I am!"

Here's what Cyd Charisse has to say about exercise:

> I exercise every day . . . it doesn't have to be anything strenuous. Everybody can walk, and walking is a fine way to use your body. But you must carry yourself straight and set a pace, swinging your leg from the hip and transferring your weight from the back foot to the front. The trouble with city walkers is they walk from the knees down . . . and backs aren't held up straight . . . Everybody should stretch every day. Animals know this. You have to use your muscles and your joints to keep them from getting stiff. Most

people when they reach middle age can't straighten their legs. Their knees are perpetually bent from lack of use.

Once more Eve had straightened her drooping shoulders, and as she rose from her chair she cautiously flexed and straightened her knees. "My knees are still flexible," she said, and a sparkle had chased away the dullness in her eyes. "And thank goodness they are, because I must rush away."

"Rushing," I said, "and unnecessary hurry are two destroyers of charm and personality."

"I know," she said, "but just this once it's important. I want to get to the grocery store before it closes, stock up on eggs, ground beef, fresh fruit, honey, yogurt, and buttermilk—and then take a long, brisk walk home!"

10

Personality in Marriage

"A GOOD marriage is one in which each appoints the other guardian of his solitude. Once the realization is accepted that *even between the closest human beings infinite distances continue to exist,* a wonderful living side by side can grow up, if they succeed in loving the distance between them which makes it possible for each to see the other whole against a wide sky!"

I quoted this advice on marriage from the letters of the German writer Rilke to the outraged young man who had just told me he was going to divorce his wife. He stopped his furious floor-pacing just long enough to light another cigarette and look at me skeptically.

"I suppose you think I'm a heel," Perry Hart said.

"It's unusual, to say the least," I said, "for a man to want a divorce for no more reason than you have."

"What do you mean, no more reason?" he asked. "My wife doesn't love me any more!"

"Has she told you so?" I asked.

"She doesn't have to tell me," he said. "All her actions show it! A lot of men might be too proud to admit it, but I married for love and companionship. What's a marriage without them?"

"And you don't have them any more?" I asked.

"Not so you could notice it," he said, coming to a halt and sitting down suddenly, wearily. "Those infinite distances between us, which you just spoke about, have become too great. They're a barrier that separates us, and there's no use in our trying to go on together."

"Suppose you tell me what caused this barrier," I said.

"Karen and I have always done everything together," he said. "I love the outdoor life—camping, hunting, fishing—and she's always gone with me."

"And what about Karen?" I asked. "Does she love the rugged outdoor life as much as you do?"

"Why, sure," he said. "Well, that is—I never asked her—but, sure, she does. But that's what our final big row was about. I'd closed a deal that brought me a fat commission, and I was going to spend it on a station wagon and new equipment for our trips— and she told me if I did she'd never go on another camping trip with me as long as she lived!"

"Maybe you should have asked her long ago just how she felt about those trips," I said.

"*She* wants to take the money and build an addition to the nursery," he said. "What do you think of that? Our baby's only four months old, and he must have a bigger nursery already!"

"Perhaps she's planning ahead," I said, "and thinking in terms of a larger family."

"Not if her actions are any criterion," Perry said. "She's shut me out like I was a stranger. She's even moved out of our bedroom and sleeps on a day bed in the nursery!"

"Don't you think you might be considered a little unreasonable," I suggested, "to expect a woman with a four-month-old baby to go on a camping trip with you?"

"Unreasonable?" he said. "Of course not! We have a good nurse for little Perry—or we did have until Karen fired her and decided to do all the work herself, thinking she'd punish me. We can get the nurse back any time, or another one just as good. But Karen has changed. It's her fault that we're not compatible any more."

"Compatibility in marriage," I said, "consists of more than

merely liking the same things. Men and women are bound to differ frequently on almost any subject you can mention. They almost never think alike or react in the same way, but they can be compatible if they have only two things in common—love for each other and tolerance for the differences between them."

The couple who never disagree and wouldn't speak a harsh word to each other for the world are much more likely to be sexually incompatible than a man and wife who argue out their difficulties. It's impossible to live intimately with a person and never become annoyed, irritated, or just plain furious. To play the sweetness-and-light role when you're seething inside is hypocritical, hard on your nerves, and may, by indirect blocking, turn you into a frustrating, hostile sex partner.

Tastes are as many and as varied as personalities. That's why you often hear "What does *she* see in that big, blustery show-off?" or "What does *he* see in that quiet, mousy little thing?" It's axiomatic (if not always authentic) that opposites attract. Two personalities living under the same roof should complement each other, but they certainly needn't have similar temperaments, tastes, or desires, nor need they enjoy the same diversions.

Why should we want our partner in marriage to mirror our moods, and echo our thoughts, when a good, rousing difference of opinion can be more stimulating?

The solitude that Rilke mentions can be tremendously important, even in marriage. Or perhaps I should say, *especially* in marriage. A place to go when the world is too much with you. A retreat where you can renew yourself, away from pressures, work, and people.

If that retreat can be shared with the one you love, well and good. But if the object of your affections hates retreats and loves the confusing, bustling hurdy-gurdy of life, why make an issue of it? It will only end in arguments, unhappiness, and the you-don't-love-me-or-you'd-love-what-I-like wail.

The retreat needn't be far away or inaccessible to others. If you're a man, it may be no farther than a workshop in your basement. Dr. Ira M. Altshuler, a Detroit psychiatrist, tells us, succinctly, "The American male goes soon and silent to his grave because he keeps his big mouth shut—when he ought to be letting off steam!"

In your retreat, workshop, or the like, you can let off steam. You can pound, bang, hammer, and saw away, working off your tensions and hidden hostilities until you feel fit to face the world and your wife once more.

The marked emphasis on "togetherness" is hazardous for many marriages, and the strong, emotional attraction between a man and a woman sometimes dies out when exposed unduly to it. There is, of course, no hard and fast rule. Again, it depends on the individuals involved and their respective needs. These needs are practically never the same for any two people.

The romantic glow of courtship can and should continue through marriage and sex adjustment, and grow into a deep, pervasive achievement, with mutual respect, love, and understanding. *And this does not have to include a complete sharing of common interests.*

"Real love is the main ingredient of a happy marriage," I said. "If you have that, you can make the necessary adjustments, see the other person's point of view and make allowances for it, because real love contains selflessness and doesn't try to dictate or dominate."

"That's just it," Perry said. "Karen always tried to dictate to me—about my eating habits."

"Oh, did she?" I asked, unable to hide the gleam of sudden interest in my eyes. "In what way?"

"In every way," he said, "but about breakfast in particular. She always got up early and cooked a big breakfast and insisted that we both eat it."

"Don't you enjoy a good, hearty breakfast?" I asked.

"Before I was married I never ate breakfast," he said, "except when I was on a hunting or fishing trip. Nothing like the outdoors to give me an appetite; I eat everything in sight—hot dogs, baked beans, or fried mush—anything! But you know, I got so I really enjoyed those man-sized breakfasts of meat and eggs, fruit, and cooked cereal that Karen fixed for me. I seemed to get more work done, and I didn't get tired and irritable by the middle of the morning, the way I do now."

"What do you mean," I asked, "the way you do now? Don't you still eat a good breakfast?"

"Not any more," he said. "Karen hasn't cooked breakfast for me since she fired the nurse and we started quarreling."

"Doesn't she eat any breakfast herself?" I asked.

"I don't know," he said. "Probably not. She's too busy fussing over the baby to pay much attention to what she eats, or to me, either."

"Then I'm not surprised that you two are quarreling," I said, "nor that you become exhausted and irritable halfway through your day's work, and are even to the point where you're ready to divorce your wife for no good reason."

"Now, wait a minute!" he said. "I've tried to patch this up. I asked Karen to go out to dinner and to a show with me, because that's what she used to like—but she wouldn't budge from the house. Wouldn't leave the baby. She said she preferred his company to mine, because I was dishonest."

"What did she mean by that?" I asked.

"Who knows what a woman means by *anything?*" he said. "But I asked her, and she told me. She said I was trying to bribe her with a dinner and a show so she wouldn't refuse to go on the camping trip with me."

"And were you?" I asked.

"Sure, I was," he said. "So now I'm dishonest. I'm also tired of asking my wife for favors. I'm sick of going to the corner drug-store for a sandwich, when I'd like to have dinner in my own home—"

"No breakfast," I said, "and sandwiches for dinner! I'm not surprised that you and your wife are quarreling. The only reason you haven't had a real knockdown drag-out fight is because you'd both be too weak for it, the way you've been eating. Karen hasn't strengthened the bond between you—nor strengthened your respective bodies!—by letting you go to work without breakfast, and by failing to make your homecoming a happy, relaxing occasion, with a nourishing dinner waiting for you."

"I told you it was her fault," he said, "when you started blaming me."

"Both of you are to blame," I said.

"Sometimes I think Karen just married me for security," he said.

"Didn't you also expect marriage to bring you a form of security that you hadn't known before?" I asked.

"I certainly did expect a home and companionship," he said, "and love—which I'm not getting!"

"Love is primarily giving, not receiving," I said. "If your desire to be loved crowds out your ability to love someone, you're narcissistic (named for the Greek god Narcissus, who fell in love with his own image), which is the earliest stage of your emotional development and should be outgrown. The good marriage is one in which there is a mutual give-and-take, one which contributes to the growth and personality development of both partners. Never use it for the satisfaction and development of one personality to the exclusion of the other."

"What do you do," asked Perry, "when your wife refuses to have anything to do with sex?"

"Sexual maladjustment is often a symptom of personality maladjustment," I said. "While the emotionally mature person is capable of making a good sexual adjustment in spite of other domestic difficulties, the immature person approaches sex with conflicts and fears. On the face of it, it seems that your wife is being selfish and immature. But she has a four-month-old baby, and pregnancy makes such demands upon a woman that she still may be under par physically, unless she's been extremely well-nourished both during pregnancy and afterward. Many women aren't left with an adequate supply of nutrients for themselves, because the needs of the baby are met first. And from your own personal account, both you and your wife are decidedly undernourished at present."

"Karen did have some trouble with anemia," he said.

"Anemia, in general," I said, "means that the body isn't fed adequately to produce enough red corpuscles—the conveyers that carry the body's supply of oxygen. If your wife is anemic, her fatigue can amount to a continuous, unrelenting dead-tiredness. Naturally, a woman in this condition hasn't the pep or energy for any extracurricular activities."

"I never thought of her as being sick," Perry said. "Of course I wouldn't leave her in a case like that."

"Unless she ate enough protein foods during her pregnancy," I said, "her glandular balance may have become disturbed."

Protein nutrition is essential to sexual performance. It also enables the pituitary gland to function well, and this gland (situated at the base of the brain) produces in turn the special hormones which stimulate the sex organs to produce other hormones necessary for normal sexual activity. These hormones can't be produced in adequate quantities in the person whose diet is seriously lacking in protein and the B vitamins: and a lack of some minerals, manganese in particular, has been found to cause a loss in mating interest, and sometimes sterility.

"Is it possible," Perry asked, "that just skipping breakfast and grabbing sandwiches for dinner can be so serious?"

"So serious," I said, "that it can wreck your health, your life, and your marriage. Your wife had the excuse of pregnancy, which took the initial toll of her strength, combined with her poor eating habits of recent date. But you've been deliberately careless. You both need to eat plenty of high-protein foods (meat, fish, poultry, eggs, cheese and other dairy products) three times a day. Supplement these meals with a really complete vitamin-mineral food supplement. Don't overlook the importance of lecithin granules! And get back to that good, hearty breakfast you say Karen used to cook for you."

"*Used to* is right," he said. "She hasn't done that for some time."

"Well, you can cook, can't you?" I asked.

"Huh?" he said.

"Surely you used to cook on those camping trips, didn't you?" I asked.

"Sure," he said, "but that was different."

"Try cooking an appetizing breakfast for the two of you," I said, "for a few mornings. You'll both feel so much better, and she'll be so delighted that you're co-operating with her that she'll soon take over—and feed you better than ever!"

"You think it'll work out that way?" he asked. "We've both been pretty irritable lately."

"You could hardly help being irritable," I said, "on your woefully inadequate diet. And irritability is one of the outstanding personality traits that undermines married love."

"What are the others?" he asked. "Between the two of us, Karen and I may have a monopoly on them!"

"Here they are," I said, "and if you do have a monopoly on them, remember that in a sound environment and with the good health and stable emotions that come from a balanced, nutritious diet, all of these home-wrecking qualities can be minimized and many of them eliminated:

1. *Stinginess.* The person close with money is likely to be miserly with his love, with his time, patience, consideration, and sympathy. Marriage with someone who can't give freely of himself can be almost intolerable.

2. *Selfishness.* The person who is so much in love with himself (the narcissist again!) that he can have no real love for anybody is a bad matrimonial bet. He approaches everything, including marriage, with the thought, "What's in it for *me*?"

3. *Irritability.* The nervous, high-strung person is easily angered, often unreasonable, frequently exploding over trifles that the well-adjusted person would take in stride. This type is difficult to live with because of his unpredictable moods.

4. *Infallibility.* Usually the victim of a deep-rooted inferiority complex, this person can't bear criticism and has to prove that

he's right, even when he's wrong. The character who never admits to a mistake can turn *you* into an irritable person.

5. *Suspicion.* If you can't trust the one you love, you're not a good candidate for marriage. You're the person who never lets his guard down for fear somebody will take advantage of you. Who can be happy and relaxed under such circumstances?

6. *Repressed hostility.* As mentioned before, talk things out, argue if necessary, or let off steam by work or physical exertion. Anything that will bring your hostilities out of their hiding place and into the open.

"I recognize myself," Perry said, "and a good deal of Karen in almost every one of those home-wrecking personality traits. I don't think we used to have them, but we have developed them during these past months that we've been so fatigue-ridden, apparently due to our irregular and skimpy meals."

"The healthy man or woman," I said, "is far less likely to develop the irritating personality quirks that play havoc with happiness in marriage. To get the most out of life in general, and married life in particular, you need the endurance, the enthusiasm, vigor, and sense of well-being that go with a well-nourished body."

Nerves are steadier, bodies are sturdier, and emotions more stable in the fortunate well-fed ones. The whole marital outlook is bright and optimistic when you sit down to appetizing high-protein, vitamin, and mineral meals in a happy, relaxed frame of mind.

Isn't it rather absurd, in the face of these facts, to skimp on breakfast or skip it entirely, or to limit your life-giving protein intake and stuff yourself on devitalizing carbohydrates—the starches and sugars?

High-protein meals needn't be expensive, if your budget requires careful watching. Of course if you like New York cut sirloin steak and your pocketbook permits it, there's no problem. But if you need to cut corners, ground round contains just as much high-grade protein as filet mignon and sirloin. Cottage cheese and powdered skim milk are excellent and inexpensive sources of protein. Try adding dry skim milk to scrambled eggs or meat loaf for improved flavor and all those extra grams of protein!

Instead of spending money on devitalized prepared breakfast foods, doughnuts, and doughy sweet rolls, buy eggs (you need at least one a day), meat, steel-cut oats, whole-grain cereal, or millet seed. This last makes a delicious, nutritious, and comparatively little-known cereal, high in protein, rich in vitamins A and E, an excellent source of thiamine and riboflavin, and a good source of other B-complex vitamins.

Millet contains every one of the ten essential amino acids, and its protein is equal in value to animal protein. If it were necessary, life and health could be sustained on millet alone, as it is a completely balanced grain—which certainly is not true of any other cereal.

Travelers have long noted that the men and women in northern China are taller and stronger than their countrymen in southern China. For many centuries the principal food in northern China has been millet—not rice, which is the mainstay of diet in most of the country.

Money spent on wholesome, energizing, life-giving foods is an investment which will pay dividends of health, happiness, vigor, and longevity.

"I've changed my mind about a divorce," Perry said. "I've decided that my marriage is worth fighting for—it's even worth cooking for! I'm going to get up and cook a big, hearty breakfast for both of us every day—at least until Karen's health improves and she becomes more compatible and responsive."

"A woman may become unresponsive through malnutrition, exhaustion, or illness," I said, "or because there's a neglect of tenderness, warmth, and little everyday affections on the part of her husband, and then suddenly out of apparent indifference, a demand for intimacy. But for both husbands and wives, health and vitality, that are built and maintained by planned nutrition, remain the strongest safeguard of a happy sex life and a successful marriage."

11

Starches and Sugars Are Personality Wreckers!

MORE than half the American populace stays on a perpetual drunk. In other words, a sugar jag that gradually undermines the entire personality.

The ardent antisaloon leaguer who points a pious finger at the village drunk, and then goes home to three meals a day of heavy starch dishes, pies, cakes, rich puddings, plus munchings of bonbons and bottles of sweetened beverages, is equally as intemperate as the old soak who tanks up at the corner tavern.

Proof? Ask any doctor who recommends abstinence from sweets and starches to obese patients or to those suffering from diabetes. He has had plenty of experience with the cheating done by these sugar-and-starch addicts. They cannot refrain from sneaking a portion here, a bite there, despite the fact that their health—sometimes their lives—depends on a drastically curtailed consumption of sweets and rich foods. No chronic alcoholic going through "the cure" can invent more excuses for cheating than these "sweets drunkards."

They protest that there is no harm in an innocent piece of chocolate candy or an oversized piece of butterscotch pie. It's food, isn't it? Yes and no.

Carbohydrates (sweets and starches) are converted in the human system into a sugar; and in great quantities this sugar gives the identical satisfaction as that experienced by an alcoholic when he yields to his cravings. And satisfying the craving for candies, rich desserts, soft drinks, white breads, and other high-carbohydrate foods may result in a physical condition which leaves the partaker in a state of complete "food inebriation." Whenever a person is "food drunk" on too many sweets and starches, his nerves can be wrecked just as surely as if he were a chronic alcoholic.

Moreover, the sugar-and-starch addict does not eat balanced meals. Raw green salads are "horse fodder" in his opinion, while fresh fruits are merely something whose flavors are imitated in the candies, sundaes, and soft drinks which he craves every day. He must have them because they give him a lift, just as the tippler or heavy smoker must indulge himself when nervous, tired, or low-spirited.

This urge for a needed lift seizes the sugar-and-starch fiend at frequent intervals during the day; then off he hies himself to the soda fountain, the candy counter—or to the kitchen for another piece of lemon pie.

Finally, after he has made a hopeless addict of himself and his whole personality is affected, he begins to feel weak, run-down, irritable, jittery whenever he cannot obtain that needed lift. If something detains him at his desk so that he is unable to run out with the gang for his afternoon "shot" of some patented soft drink, he actually shows the strain; his mind refuses to concentrate, his nerves jump, he grows irritable.

Have you ever heard someone say, "I simply cannot take one piece of candy, then stop. I must have *all I want,* or none"? Are such persons any different than the liquor addict who must abstain completely, because the mere sight, smell, or taste of alcohol will set him off on a prolonged drinking bout?

I sometimes wonder whether we Americans, generations hence, will not finally eat ourselves into a state of decadence as a nation. It may be that someday, in the centuries to come, our cravings for sweets and starches will reduce us to the same pitiable condition as that of the once proud Andean Indian tribes of South America who are now nothing but shells of men and women, all because generations of their forebears chewed the coco leaf. Dull in mind, almost animal-like in behavior, they go on using the "green drug" which has debased their race for centuries.

Perhaps you think I am too harsh in my comparison of America's carbohydrate addicts and the South American coco-leaf chewers. I shall not ask you to take my word for the authenticity of this comparison. Here is the opinion of the medical profession: too many concentrated starch or sugar foods can produce a low blood-sugar level, *hypoglycemia.*

Why is hypoglycemia serious? Because the brain, the same as all other organs of the body, recieves its fuel from the diet. However, the brain can use only sugar which is manufactured by the body from the carbohydrates it receives in the diet. Unlike many of the body tissues, the brain cannot store its fuel supply; sugar must be supplied to it constantly through the bloodstream. That is, the brain cannot function properly when the blood-sugar level is too low.

"That is ridiculous," you are probably going to say. "First, he says the brain must have plenty of sugar; then, he contradicts himself by stating that too much sugar can cause a low sugar level in the blood. The man does not know what he is talking about!"

I will grant that this does sound paradoxical. But here is the explanation: A hormone called *insulin,* which is produced by the pancreas, controls the level of sugar in the bloodstream. In other words, insulin is the sugar administrator in the blood. When the body is overloaded with sweets and starches, the pancreas is forced to step up production of insulin. As a consequence, too much sugar is removed from the blood because *too much insulin* has been manufactured to control a temporary situation. And then, with the blood depleted of its normal amount of sugar, the brain cannot do its best work because the fuel supply has been decreased. The whole thing works in a vicious circle;

in order to give the taste buds a "sweet treat," we actually deprive the brain of its vital food supply.

What are the signs of low blood sugar caused by overeating concentrated carbohydrates? If you have a craving for sweets and starches in excessive amounts, and especially if you experience an acute desire for them between meals, you had better watch out! This is the first sign of a low blood-sugar level, either already at hand or due to arrive soon.

When the blood-sugar level falls way below normal, these symptoms show up: fits of depression or irritability; jittery nerves; slowed-up reactions; absent-mindedness; unstable emotions; hazy thinking; erratic sex behavior.

In other words, the entire course of a person's life may be affected by an excessive intake of sweets and starches. The truth behind this startling fact is beginning to take root among medical scientists.

Dr. Joseph Wilder, a New York neurologist, wrote in the *Journal of Criminal Psychopathology:*

> The existence of a direct relationship between subnormal blood sugar level and criminality will be surprising only to those who are unfamiliar with the manifestations of induced or spontaneous hypoglycemia. The literature shows that this very young offspring of medicine has a criminal record comparable to that of certain mental diseases.

Cases from Dr. Wilder's own clinical records include sexual perversion, assault and battery, embezzlement, mayhem, arson. Each defendant in these cases was suffering from hypoglycemia.

One woman patient of Dr. Wilder had suffered from a low blood-sugar level for years. She developed hysterical attacks. During these spells, she became extremely weak, incoherent, and emotionally unstable. She threw objects at her husband, and evidenced a "morbid craving for sweets."

Dr. Wilder says that "persons suffering from hypoglycemia are likely to be convicted for crimes of which they are innocent because of their lapses of memory . . . confabulations and hallucinations, or the erroneous impression of laziness or malingering which they may convey may be held against them."

Strangely enough, such symptoms are very much like those which accompany *insulin shock,* the condition suffered by diabetes victims when given an overdose of insulin.

Diabetes, of course, is a disease characterized by too much sugar in the blood, plus the inability of the pancreas to manufacture enough insulin to control the situation. Therefore, insulin must be administered by hypodermic: when an overdose is given to the victim of diabetes, his reactions are similar to those evidenced by persons suffering chronically from a low blood-sugar level—who likewise have been "overdosed" with insulin by the pancreas.

Needless to say, persons whose brains are not performing 100 per cent because of a low blood-sugar level are not going to behave as they should, either at home or in their jobs—or as citizens of their community or nation.

Dr. Wilder warns against employing victims of hypoglycemia in positions requiring great responsibility and constant alertness. He even advocates refusing driver's licenses to these persons of subnormal brain and nerve reactions.

The wicked thing about a low blood-sugar level is that wrong meals can cause this dangerous body condition in a mere matter of hours! Scientists report that a low blood-sugar level can result *three hours after eating a meal excessively high in sugar or starch.* Of course, the condition is only temporary—at least as an aftermath to that one particular meal. But it does not require a very agile imagination to realize what happens when meal after meal throughout the years is habitually top-heavy with sweets and starches, to say nothing of the between-meal indulgences in candies, pastries, and soda pop.

Dr. Wilder also mentions willful destruction of property as a frequent symptom of hypoglycemia: "Patients not only damage things when fighting but often break dishes and pieces of furniture out of mere destructiveness. One case is reported of boys who smashed expensive and prized possessions only."

Carbohydrate addicts are not limited to any particular age group nor to any one sex. Men, women, and children of all ages are its victims. Leading medical and dietetic journals often call attention to the dangerous effects of too many carbohydrates; they caution against the too-starchy, too-sweet foods that commonly go into the lunches packed for school children and for working men and women.

Ask the man of great abdominal girth what free indulgences in sugars and starches have done for him. And in the wheezy voice of the short-of-breath, characteristic of the very obese, he will admit—if he is honest—that he learned too late the undermining effects of those foods whose nutritional values are a delusion and a snare.

Ask the slim, peppy partner who can outlast anyone else on the dance floor; ask the glamorous actress of stage and movie fame; ask the tennis player who has just won a championship match; ask any modern American girl, blooming with health and beauty—ask any of these what they think of sweet, starchy foods as an item of regular diet. And most of them will shrug off the question as too obvious to require a serious answer.

A tragic number of persons spend their entire lives—and savings—in a vain quest for health. In more cases than are realized, the secret of their failure lies in the ever-open candy box; in the bakery abounding with white breads, fluffy cakes, and tempting pastries.

Excessive carbohydrates in the diet will result ultimately in a serious deficiency of vitamin B_1, because sugars and starches will burn up this vitamin so vitally needed for strong nerves. Sweets and heavy starch foods also tend to cloy the appetite so that not enough wholesome, health-building foods are eaten. As a result, deficiencies of other essential vitamins and minerals will be built up through low intake of the natural foods; unburned fat may accumulate in the tissues, causing obesity and placing an unnecessary burden on the heart, arteries, and other organs. By this time, the victim of excessive sweets and starches is nervous, highly fatigued, slowed-down mentally—he is actually ill.

Eating meals heavy with carbohydrates is a habit easy to acquire; even more so for the person of moderate income unfortunate enough to be sentenced to almost constant meals in low-priced restaurants. Carbohydrate foods—macaroni, bread puddings, rice—are easy to serve and produce greater profits for the proprietor. However, the effort required on the part of the diner to obtain well-balanced meals will bring its own reward in better health and clearer thinking.

The discipline needed to exercise will power and self-denial will achieve a certain mental lift which, in itself, is worth striving for. Pass up that serving of chocolate pie because you know it will throw your balanced diet all out of kilter, and you will spend the rest of the day in a glow of self-righteousness because "you had it in you to be strong."

On the other hand, eat the pie when you know you should not, and you will hate yourself for being a weakling with no strength of character!

The first step in overcoming an addiction to excessive sugars and starches is to make sure that all meals are well-balanced. This means that the daily intake of food must contain the correct proportion of protein, fat, liquid, vitamins, minerals, as well as carbohydrates. *By no means, should all carbohydrates be left out of the diet.* That would be as wrong as including too many sugars and starches. However, the carbohydrates in a well-balanced diet must come from natural foods—honey, fruits, vegetables, whole grains—and not from the devitalized foods—rich desserts, white breads, confectioners' products, and carbonated beverages—all of which provide sugars and starches in their very worst form.

Further, a craving for sweets has been traced in numerous instances to a serious deficiency of calcium in the body. Perhaps a person's inability to control his or her appetite for chocolates and pastries is not solely a matter of will power; a systemic lack of calcium may be causing the craving. If you have tried to break the sweets habit—honestly tried—and have failed, I recommend that you increase your intake of calcium through the use of more calcium-rich foods, supplemented by mineral tablets containing both calcium and sodium. The chances are ten to one that this next time you swear off sweets you will succeed in passing the candy store and the bakery instead of walking into them.

And the chances are, too, that the more wholesome foods— meat, fish, cheese, eggs, green vegetables, fruits, dairy products— will take on new, more exciting flavors for you than you have ever found in them before. Your sweet-deadened taste buds will come alive and seek out the hidden goodness of plain, wholesome foods.

A great percentage of hypochondriacs, semi-invalids, and bed-ridden cases need never have been robbed of the joy of vigorous living if they could have been protected against the sugar-starch evil which hangs over too many dinner tables.

I shall always remember the missionary whom I met in Seattle. She and her husband had just returned after years of service among the Eskimos within the Arctic Circle. Her great sorrow was that during the latter years of their work among these primitive people, fur traders had invaded their settlement, bringing in white flour, refined sugar, and candy to exchange for pelts. It was not long, the missionary told me, before the health of their congregation began to suffer.

The Eskimos forsook their former diet of natural food and lived mainly off half-cooked dough heavily sweetened with white sugar; the youngsters whose teeth had always been perfect came crying with toothache to the mission house; school and church attendance dropped sharply because of the increased sickness; influenza and pneumonia carried off great numbers of the older persons.

Personality changes began to take place: the hitherto peaceable tribe began quarreling among themselves over petty incidents, even to the point of violence and murder. From teachers and pastors, the missionaries were changed into doctors and judges. Civilization had come to that little Eskimo settlement; its inhabitants had been converted into sugar-and-starch addicts.

12

Raise Your Blood Sugar—and Sweeten Your Personality

IF YOU are either a full-time or a part-time sourpuss—and are tired of being one—it's time you learned a little more about blood sugar and how it can help you to a sweetened personality! A large number of people who formerly looked at the world through the windows of a pickle factory were pleasantly surprised to find how relatively easy this personality sweetening process can be.

How does one go about the business of sweetening an unpleasant personality? It entails a little more than the superficial façade many feel is so important to impress others and make them like us. A phony, put-on personality is too transparent not to be detected. That is one thing you *don't* want!

You may have practiced smiling in front of your mirror, thinking you could fool everybody with simulated sweetness. But it's no use. The minute you forget to turn on that insincere smile, the corners of your mouth droop and your brows knit in an ugly, irritated frown.

You simply don't *feel* sweet and charming. You'd hate to say out loud just how you do feel, but *beat* is a fairly descriptive word. The beat generation! Whoever thought that up must have had you in mind. But surely a whole generation can't feel as you do: sunk away down in a slough of despond, dead-tired, half-sick, inefficient, disgusted, and bad-tempered—and where's the escape from it?

There is none, you think. Or if there is, you're sure that you'll never find it. You haven't the energy or the initiative to look for a solution. Is this what it's like to be old? But you're not old—not even middle-aged.

Then why do you have all of these aches and pains? The tension in the back of your neck and shoulders, the stiff and aching knees, the stomach pains characteristic of ulcers, and the tenderness in the upper left abdomen, the devastating headaches, the restlessness that keeps you from relaxing even though you're exhausted, and the inability to concentrate or make a decision?

Still more frightening are the sudden attacks of heart palpitation that occasionally seize you in the middle of the night, so severe that your bed seems to shake in unison with your heart's thumping. Your doctor can find nothing organically wrong, and diagnoses it as "cardiac neurosis," which means a nervous condition that manifests itself in the symptoms associated with organic heart disease.

Not one, but many ailments seem to assail you at every turn. You snarl at your family, snap at your fellow workers, and hate your boss. He used to be a nice fellow, too, but now he's impossible.

Who's impossible? Take a good, long look at yourself in that mirror. What you see is far from pleasant: a sallow skin, dull, clouded eyes that seem to lack the intelligent look they once possessed, and deep lines that temper, tension, and fatigue have etched on a once smooth face.

How did this happen to *you*? This excessive weariness and apathy that almost amount to stupidity? And what's happened to the personality you used to have—your optimism, verve, friendliness, vitality and enthusiasm for living that used to make every day an adventure?

It isn't *possible* for one's personality to undergo such a drastic and woebegone change. Or is it?

Indeed it is! It's happened to you. And now the question is, what can you do about it?

First of all, you can go and have a blood-sugar test. The six-hour Glucose Tolerance Test can determine whether or not you have low blood sugar, which is perhaps the only ailment that can account for such varied and multitudinous symptoms.

So far, I have mentioned low blood sugar only as it occurs periodically in the normal person, due to an insufficient protein intake or infrequent meals, the skipping of breakfast, in particular. Even this can cause a distressing number of symptoms which are difficult to diagnose, and the remedy for it has been discussed in previous chapters.

But now we're up against something more serious. Hyperinsulinism—which has been called variously "sugar starvation," "the hunger disease," and "chronic fatigue"—is the exact opposite of diabetes. The diabetic has to take insulin to stay alive, while the victim of hyperinsulinism manufactures his own insulin—and too much of it!—in the islands of Langerhans, which have become too sensitive in response to the metabolic demand. The liver converts sugar into starch, and doesn't leave enough in the circulating blood. Most of your body cells receive nourishment from various sources, but your brain's sustenance is from glucose alone, and that from moment to moment, as it can't store sugar for future use as other organs can.

Hyperinsulinism, like the villain in the cheap melodrama, wears many disguises, which makes it difficult to recognize. And like this same villain, it's sneaky, creeping up on you slowly, insidiously, with innumerable and hard to diagnose symptoms.

Dr. Seale Harris was the first to report on hyperinsulinism (in 1924, when he was professor of medicine at the University of Alabama), using the prefix *hyper-* to indicate that it resulted from an excessive secretion of the hormone by the patient's own insulin apparatus . . . the direct opposite of the diabetic, who has too little insulin and is obliged to take it in sufficient quantity for him to remain alive.

The islands of Langerhans are our insulin apparatus, sometimes unpredictable and subject to aberrations, besides being easily oversensitized. And while hyperinsulinism *always* produces a deficiency in blood sugar, there are other conditions which may cause this deficiency.

There are four different, but similar, forms of hyperinsulinism. They differ in cause, severity, and prescribed treatment, the most severe being a malignant tumor (insuloma, with 100 per cent mortality) of the islands of Langerhans, which luckily is rarely encountered.

The second type is a benign tumor which grows in the pancreas and, by irritating the islands of Langerhans, causes them to secrete too much insulin. The third kind is caused by a general enlargement of the island tissue, but minus any protruding lumps or tumors, benign or otherwise.

The fourth form of hyperinsulinism is the most common of all, the functional type called hypoglycemia, which is one way of saying "low blood sugar." In this form, the islands of Langerhans seem to be perfectly healthy and sound in type and structure except for one thing: they produce more insulin than they should.

At a most conservative estimate, the number of persons suffering from hyperinsulinism in the United States is well over a million. And if all of the undiagnosed cases were counted, no doubt it would be twenty times that.

These are the persons who are often called neurotic, because their quest for health takes them from one doctor to another. Always exhausted, defeated, almost hopeless, they try in vain to find relief from their various types of suffering, which range from chronic fatigue, nervousness, anxiety, stomach pains, heart pains, and palpitation to apparent mental disorders, including confusion, crying spells, lack of co-ordination, dizziness, and sometimes complete unconsciousness or stupor.

Are you the nervous, high-strung type? If so, you probably consume your blood sugar through the very tenseness of your actions and attitudes. Your symptoms of irritability, weakness, exhaustion, and impatience (indicating a personality that *needs* sweetening!) generally appear four to six hours after a meal, and a delay in eating accentuates the symptoms.

If you've eaten a good breakfast, your meals are usually frequent enough during the day to prevent a decided drop in blood sugar, if your hyperinsulinism is a mild case. But around two or three o'clock in the morning enough time has elapsed since your last meal for your blood sugar to drop below the normal physiological minimum. That's the time you are most subject to asthmatic attacks or unnerving, fluttering or pounding palpitation of your heart.

Are you accident prone? The type of person who is always getting bumped, banged, bruised, cut, or burned? Do you have more traffic violations than your ability as a driver warrants?

Dr. Sidney A. Portis has written much about the relation between fatigue states and accidents. Out of his experience, he tells us, "A good breakfast and frequent feedings during the day are essential to the prevention of accidents . . . Army efficiency engineers, investigating almost 1,000 accident cases . . . found that a large majority of the injured workers *came to their jobs without breakfast;* resulting fatigue and carelessness had struck them down."

When you drive that efficient machine, your body, too hard, and give it the wrong kind of food—or not enough—the disastrous results reveal themselves finally in a confusing conglomeration of uncomfortable or painful symptoms in the neuromuscular, respiratory, gastrointestinal, or cardiovascular systems. Any one of these symptoms might easily mean hypoglycemia.

One of the surest ways to develop hypoglycemia is to overload on starches and sugars, as discussed in the previous chapter, eat only one meal a day, and consume cup after cup of black coffee the rest of the time to stave off hunger.

If you are to think clearly and work efficiently, you require a blood-sugar level high enough to supply the demands of nerve, muscle, and brain cells. To function without it places your body and brain under a strain which is injurious to them.

Your brain, in particular, absolutely must have nourishment (glucose) during every minute of every hour. And let me repeat: it is the protein foods, *not sugar,* that maintain your blood sugar at a high level. Sugar is forbidden, as it causes a sharp rise in your blood sugar, then a sudden, disastrous drop. The jump in that level is what is significant, rather than the actual level—a rise from 80 to 140 has about the same effect as a rise from 180 to 240.

When the blood-sugar level falls too low, the adrenal glands get busy and pump adrenalin into the blood, which they do in an emergency to enable you to fight or defend yourself. Only this time there's no emergency and you have nothing to fight, but the adrenalin has to do *something.* What it does is bring on the flushing, palpitation of the heart, and convulsions such as a diabetic has when he's taken an overdose of insulin. But you're not a diabetic, and it's your own oversupply of insulin that's done the damage!

There is complete agreement among doctors upon the fundamentals of the diet for low blood sugar: *a good, hearty breakfast, positively no sugar,* a snack between breakfast and luncheon, another in the middle of the afternoon, and *always something to eat before going to bed.*

Lists of taboos vary in a slight degree, but almost all include, *no smoking before meals!* Tests show that one cigarette before breakfast is more harmful than a whole pack afterward. A small quantity of concentrated nicotine can be fatal (such as the amount used in insecticides), but the acids and tars in cigarettes are more injurious than the minute amount of nicotine that they contain.

Are you so tired and grumpy when you come home from work that the children hide and your wife doesn't dare speak to you until after you've had your dinner? A midafternoon protein snack might sweeten your disposition enough to surprise your family and have them come running to meet you, instead of avoiding you and saying to each other, "Keep out of Pop's way—he's pooped again tonight!"

When you allow your blood sugar to remain at a low level— because of an insufficient breakfast, too little protein, too much sugar, or infrequent meals—you are literally starving your body's cells, especially your brain cells.

Don't permit your brain and body to remain chronically under-nourished!

The effect of starvation on the various cells is not the same in each individual, which accounts for the many varied and mis-leading symptoms of hyperinsulinism. The weakest cells are the first to show the wear and tear of undernourishment, but we have no soothsayer, medicine man, or ouija board to tell us beforehand just which of our cells are the weakest—with the possible exception of the brain cells, which we know are the most easily undernourished, and consequently, perhaps fastest to deteriorate.

Failure to eat a good breakfast is one of the wrongs responsible for allowing your blood sugar to run too low for the efficient use of your mind and body. Thousands of blood analyses have shown that even a normal person can have as low as 80 milligrams of sugar in 100 cc. (about one-half cup) of his blood, if he hasn't eaten for twelve hours.

You need from 90 to 95 for energy, efficiency, and clear thinking.

If you haven't eaten an adequate breakfast, weariness, ir-ritability, and lassitude set in. And if your blood sugar goes down to 65 milligrams, your stomach growls, you have a craving for sweets (which you should *not* eat, under any circumstances!), and you begin to feel weak and perhaps a little dizzy.

A drop in blood sugar can change your whole personality. As it continues to fall below normal, you progressively become more irritable, moody, depressed, grouchy, inefficient, and un-co-opera-tive.

A mother once brought her teen-age son to see me. He had become unruly, surly, and hard to get along with. His schoolwork had fallen off, and he was well on his way to becoming a juvenile delinquent. A finicky eater, he refused breakfast, ate little meat, and few vegetables, but would polish off several helpings of dessert, which she allowed him to have, since "he received so little nourishment otherwise."

As we sat and talked, the boy's attention wandered. He was indifferent and lethargic. The only interest he showed was in a chocolate bar which he took from his pocket and ate ravenously.

"He's always hungry," his mother said, "but only for sweets. That's about all he'll eat."

"Has he ever had a test for low blood sugar?" I asked.

"Low blood sugar?" she said. "I never heard of it."

"Lots of people suffering from it have never heard of it," I said, "but, unfortunately, that doesn't prevent their having it."

"He couldn't have low blood sugar," she said; "he eats more sugar than anything else."

"Eating sweets," I said, "as strange as it seems, is one of the surest ways of causing low blood sugar (hyperinsulinism or hypoglycemia). Take him for a test, and if he has it and is put on the prescribed diet, he'll be allowed no sugar at all."

Less than three months later the mother returned to see me, and her face was beaming as she shook my hand.

"You know, you were right about Roger," she said. "He had hypoglycemia, and was put on the diet. It was hard for him to stay on it until he saw the difference it was making in him. His schoolwork began to improve, and friends that had dropped him started coming by to see him again—he just isn't the same unruly boy that he was. He'd have come by here with me, but he's so busy these days. He's gone out for football, and he's on the debating team—and just a few weeks ago I thought he was headed straight for juvenile delinquency!"

It's not only possible, but highly probable that an appalling number of our juvenile deliquents are victims of low blood sugar. It is known that schizophrenics have a low blood-sugar level.

The improvement of neurotics is pronounced and rapid when proper nourishment of the brain begins, after partial cell starvation.

And what of the 16,000 persons who take their own lives each year? Among the many reasons for suicide are depression and mental confusion—two of the myriad symptoms of low blood sugar. If even one life can be saved or one juvenile delinquent made into a useful citizen, it would certainly be worth our while to look into these two grave problems from every possible angle —including the possibility of low blood sugar.

The well-known and widely read Dr. Herman N. Bundesen has this to say about it:

> If you are arrested frequently for traffic violations, if you clash often with authorities, you may be suffering from hypoglycemia . . . a drop in your blood sugar means a cut in that amount that reaches the brain . . . in hypoglycemia, the brain is deprived of its fuel and main source of energy. I think you can see how this can lead to difficulty, maybe to jail or the psychopathic ward. If the blood sugar level is cut by one third, you are apt to become dull, be unable to concentrate and have difficulty making decisions. A drop of one-half means that you will probably lose most of your will power and become confused about time and situations. Should the level drop even further, the result might be stupor, coma, hysteria, delirium, and schizophrenic symptoms.

The victim of low blood sugar should take frequent meals, so that instead of having three big rises and drops in his blood sugar, he'll have several small ones, which may in time smooth out to a normal level. The *sudden* rise in blood sugar is what stimulates the islands of Langerhans to produce an oversupply of insulin, and for that reason *no* sweets are permitted—not even honey, grape juice, or prune juice. (All other *unsweetened* juices are allowed.) A high-protein diet is most effective because the protein foods are turned into blood sugar more slowly by the body's chemistry, which eases that sudden letdown.

If you suffer from low blood sugar, here is a recommended diet to follow which, by normalizing your blood-sugar level, will enable you to regain maximum health and sweeten your personality.

DIET FOR HYPERINSULINISM

ON ARISING

One cup of warm non-fat milk. *Or* 4 ounces of juice. *Or* a half grapefruit. *Or* a medium-sized orange.

BREAKFAST

Choice of fruit (*except* bananas, dates, figs, plums, grapes, or raisins).

1 or 2 eggs with a meat patty. *Or* a small steak. *Or* 1 or 2 chops. *Or* broiled fish. *Or* a large portion of cottage cheese (try mixing a small quantity of tomato juice into it—*delicious!*).

Bread or toast: one slice with butter—but only if you *absolutely* must. (Use 100 per cent whole-grain or high-protein bread.)

Beverage: non-fat milk; weak tea made with tea bag, not brewed; *or* coffee substitute with *absolutely no caffeine.**

2 HOURS AFTER BREAKFAST

4 ounces of juice. *Or* protein concentrates in powder or tablet form.

LUNCH

Meat, eggs, fish, or cheese.

Large mixed green salad. *Or* lettuce and tomato salad. *Or* apple and nut salad. Add a small amount of French dressing or mayonnaise.

Vegetables as desired.

Bread or toast: one slice with butter—but again, only if you *absolutely* must.

---

* If you simply cannot do without coffee at breakfast—if denying yourself that morning cup of coffee will make you impossible to live with, then, for the sake of your mental equilibrium, you may have *up to* 8 ounces *only* (about a cup and a half). But it must be absolutely free of all sediment and brewed to keep caffeine-content down to a minimum. Such coffee can be made in the *Chemex* scientific coffee maker that is available in most department and housewares stores.

Dessert: Unsweetened gelatin. *Or* fresh fruit. *Or* junket (made from tablets).

Beverage: as for breakfast.

3 HOURS AFTER LUNCH

8 ounces of non-fat milk. *Or* protein concentrates in powder or tablet form.

1 HOUR BEFORE DINNER

4 ounces of juice.

DINNER

Soup, if desired. (*Not* thickened with flour.)

Large portion of meat, poultry, or fish.

Vegetables as desired.

Bread or toast: one slice with butter—but to repeat, only if you *absolutely* must.

Dessert: as for lunch.

Beverage: as for breakfast.

2 TO 3 HOURS AFTER DINNER

8 ounces of non-fat milk.

EVERY 2 HOURS UNTIL BEDTIME

4 ounces of non-fat milk. *Or* a small handful of sunflower seed kernels, almonds, or other nuts.

IMPORTANT

You will, of course, continue taking vitamins and minerals to supplement your food intake—as well as lecithin and whatever nutritional concentrates you normally use.

SOME GENERAL RULES TO OBSERVE

You may eat all of the following:

VEGETABLES

Asparagus, avocado, beets, broccoli, Brussels sprouts, cabbage, cauliflower, carrots, celery, corn, cucumbers, egg plant, Lima beans, onions, peas, radishes, sauerkraut, squash, string beans, tomatoes, turnips.

FRUITS

Apples, apricots, berries, grapefruit, melons, oranges, peaches, pineapple, tangerines. (Fruits may be raw, cooked, or canned—canned fruits must be packed in water or natural juices, not syrup—*and with no sugar.*)

MISCELLANEOUS

Nuts, mushrooms, and lettuce may be eaten as liberally as desired. For dessert eat fruit, cheese, unsweetened gelatin, junket (made with tablets, not the mix).

You may drink all of the following:

BEVERAGES

Weak tea (made with tea bag, not brewed); coffee substitutes, caffeine-free coffee (sweetened with sugar substitute, not sugar); non-fat milk; buttermilk.

JUICES

Any unsweetened fruit or vegetable juice, except prune juice or grape juice.

ALCOHOLIC AND SOFT DRINKS

Naturally, you are better off without them. But if life seems incomplete unless you have a drink, stick to: club soda, *dry* ginger ale, whiskies and other *distilled* liquors like gin, vodka, brandy, etc.

You Must Avoid Absolutely:

Candy, sugar, and all other sweets such as pie, pastries, cake, sweet rolls, sweet custards, puddings, ice cream, and sherbet.

Caffeine—coffee and strong brewed tea, all beverages containing caffeine, including the soft carbonated cola drinks, and all drinks sweetened with sugar. (See footnote on page 127.)

Potatoes, rice, grapes, plums, figs, dates, and bananas.

Spaghetti, macaroni, and noodles, (High-protein gluten products may occasionally be used.)

Wines, cordials, cocktails, and beer.

Modifications of the diet, to some slight extent, may often be permitted after three months, depending on the individual and the severity of his symptoms. But the first food on arising is important to start the body's machinery in high gear—and frequent snacks during the day to maintain that speed. This explains the great emphasis on high-protein and sugar-free food.

If you have hyperinsulinism, *coffee (or caffeine in any form) is restricted from now on.* (See footnote on page 127.)

During a business trip to a Southern town which is the home of a famous carbonated, caffeine-spiked, and sugar-laden soft drink, I was struck with the apathy of most of the persons I met. Surely, I thought, this isn't the result of the climate. I felt fine during my stay there, as did the other members of my party. What then was the reason? The consumption of this particular drink was in enormous quantities, from the smallest children to the oldest citizens. Many of them drank it instead of water, instead of coffee, fruit juices, or milk—with *all* meals, and between meals, to give them a lift.

Certainly it gave them a lift, because of its high sugar and caffeine content, but that lift was of short duration, as their blood sugar would zoom up quickly, then fall to a very low level. This necessitated another bottle of the beverage for another temporary lift—thus creating a vicious circle—and more victims of partial sugar starvation, or low blood sugar.

Such soft drinks containing sugar and caffeine constitute another *absolute taboo.*

This isn't going to be easy, you think? Perhaps not. But surely it's worth a few sacrifices to regain your health, energy, ambition, optimism, initiative, and an abundant joy in living.

If you have low blood sugar, *you cannot eat sugar or anything containing it.*

You *want* to sweeten your personality, don't you? You are tired of having people avoid you, sick of your own miserable disposition and irritable, depressed feeling, dismayed at your loss of friends and your lack of ambition. In fact, you are just plain tired, worn-out, exhausted, and with no relief in sight.

Well, here *is* relief for you. It's yours with just a little effort on your part.

Isn't it worth making that effort, even though it means throwing away your sugar bowl, coffeepot, and leaving the room, if necessary, when ice cream, pie, cake, or other pastries, and coffee are passed?

13

Exterminate Those Personality Termites!

"I'M ALL in favor of exterminating any kind of pest," you may say, "but first, I want to know just what you mean. Maybe you'd better explain what personality termites are."

It's impossible for me to tell, even if I had radar or extrasensory perception, exactly what *your* particular personality termites are. It may take a thorough, searching self-examination to disclose the precise type of termite that has fastened itself on you. The chances are that your family and friends can help in the analysis. They can see your failings with more clarity and objectivity than you can—and are usually more than willing to tell you what they are!

Personality termites are any and all of the negative emotions, fears, thoughts, opinions, prejudices, and ingrown habits that have an adverse effect upon your mental and physical health—which in turn affects your whole life.

Persistently, sometimes almost imperceptibly, they gnaw away at those basically sound structures, your mind and body, until one or the other (sometimes both!) weakens, totters, and perhaps collapses.

Don't let it happen to you! Personality termites can and should be exterminated before such serious damage is done. Better still is the ounce of prevention—make it a *ton* of prevention, if necessary—that keeps them from making you a potential victim.

Hate, fear, suspicion, tension, anxiety, anger—these and many more are personality termites which should be exterminated if you are to live at peace with yourself and your fellow man—if you are to be a well-integrated personality, capable of adjusting yourself to various persons, places and situations.

I was waiting in a restaurant for a luncheon engagement with Fred Harris. After half an hour, I decided to order my own lunch. Maybe Fred had been unavoidably detained, and there was no use getting in a dither over it, so I proceeded to enjoy my excellent steak and green salad. Halfway through the meal Fred stormed in and sat down so suddenly that the silverware on the table shook. His face was almost purple, and his forehead and upper lip were beaded with perspiration.

"Don't order anything for me," he said, "except a double Scotch and soda. I'm so angry I couldn't eat a bite!"

"You're using your anger to hurt yourself," I said, "and robbing your body of nourishment when you fail to eat because of bad temper."

"I know, I know," he said. "And I won't be able to do a lick of work this afternoon, either, but I can't help it. I'm just plain boiling mad at my boss. He never gives credit where it's due. He takes my ideas and uses them as his own, and ends up by actually believing that they *are* his! Of course that's only when the top brass approves of them. If a suggestion happens to boomerang, he passes the buck straight back to me. That's what he did today—and that's why I hate the guy!"

His double Scotch had arrived, and he took a long drink of it before he spoke again. "Half the time I'm so furious that I can't eat any lunch. And now he tells me that my work is falling off, but I notice that it's still good enough for him to steal!"

Without realizing it, Fred was harboring three destructive personality termites: anger, hatred, and suspicion.

"Whether you like it or not," I said, "your boss may be right. By skipping meals, both your mind and body become undernourished and unable to function properly. They become too weak to do the effective, creative thinking that your job in advertising demands. You let your damaging negative emotions go on a rampage because you're so under par physically that you can't control them."

"I don't *want* to control my emotions," he said. "I'd rather be mad!"

"Maybe you'll want to," I said, "when you hear what I'm going to tell you. Uncontrolled emotions are usually the sign of a chemical deficiency in the body. When you're healthy, your body, your mind, and your emotions are in balance. But when your body and mind become weakened because of inadequate nutrition, then your emotions overbalance them and gain control of your life."

"You're right about my emotions," he said. "They do seem to have gained the upper hand lately, and I haven't helped matters any with my moods. But nearly everybody I know has the same trouble. We do creative work—although lots of people would deny it!—and we work under pressure. I'm not the stolid, vegetable type, or I wouldn't be in this business."

"I realize that," I said. "But in any environment an undernourished condition of the body can produce unhealthy emotions. And it's also true that an unrealistic appraisal of the part played by your own emotions can leave you blaming others for your misfortunes or, in extreme cases, attributing them to an evil fate."

"And you think that's what I'm doing?" asked Fred.

"You're blaming your boss for what may be partly your own shortcomings," I said. "Remember that your emotional behavior and development depend upon your exterminating your particular personality termites of anger, hatred, and suspicion."

"Exterminating my *what*?" asked Fred.

"Your personality termites," I said.

"Say, that's a good way to describe them," he said. "You ought to take a job with my agency writing slogans!"

"I can't think of a better or more suitable word than termites for these destructive emotions," I said. "They literally destroy your personality by gnawing from within. They create tensions, anxieties, and worries, and if you're to function as a normal human being, hatred must be replaced with love, anger with tolerance, and suspicion with understanding."

"If I worked hard at it," he said, "in time I might learn to tolerate my boss, and even to understand him a little—but that would be going absolutely overboard for me!"

"If you can do that much," I said, "you'll find your work considerably easier. Did you ever try to hate anybody immediately after a delicious meal, eaten in pleasant surroundings with congenial friends?"

"Of course not," he said, "and you're trying to trick me! You know in a case like that a man feels mellow, broad-minded, warmhearted, and filled with friendliness."

"Exactly," I said. "So instead of skipping meals, becoming undernourished and increasingly irritable and careless in your work, why not prolong that sense of well-being indefinitely by eating *three* well-balanced high-protein meals a day?"

Dr. Charles Glen King, executive director of The Nutrition Foundation, tells us:

> Studies on proteins during the year suggest strongly that *each meal should have a proper balance of amino acids*. Proteins are composed of amino acids, each protein being made up of some of the twenty-six odd amino acids arranged together in specific chemical configurations.
>
> Each new experiment which we carry out to determine the proper amino acid balance for good nutrition gives further proof that these essential building blocks must be supplied in a ratio similar to that *in the proteins of meat, milk, eggs, fish and poultry*. These basic studies give scientific evidence for the *importance of three balanced high-protein meals each day for all people, children or adults, active or sedentary, male or female.*

The key to balanced amino acids is in variety and *regular* intake of proteins. Amino acids in whole grain seed cereals, fruits, peas, beans, and other vegetables have values in forming balanced combinations with the complete animal proteins, as whole-grain cereals with milk or meat with beans. Additional research may suggest how combinations of plant and animal proteins may be arranged to make maximum nutritional use of natural protein foods.

We know what foods are necessary to maintain optimum health for all human beings, and we know the amount necessary for the average man or woman. But is there actually a normal, average man or woman? In all probability there is not.

Body chemistry varies in each individual. Just as personality types vary and no two sets of fingerprints in the world are the same, so are there individual differences in the way the body utilizes food. One person may receive a maximum amount of nourishment out of the food he eats. Another, with faulty absorption, receives only half as much nourishment from the same amount of food.

For that reason a good vitamin-mineral food supplement is recommended, even though your meals are well-balanced and adequate.

The range of anatomical variation even among normal people is very wide—blood vessel structures, lungs, nervous systems— every part of the human body; and body chemistry is no exception. The science of nutrition has made it possible to control many diseases, and when we learn still more about the complexities of body chemistry, countless more may be controlled or prevented.

"When you skip a meal or eat too little protein, you set the stage for hatred and anger by letting your blood sugar drop below normal," I told Fred. "And if you want to be able to stand up to conditions of stress, you should take a good vitamin-mineral food supplement containing a better than average amount of the B-complex vitamins, which are known as the antifatigue, antitoxic, and antistress factors."

When Dr. Tom Spies, noted nutritionist, gave a number of

patients vitamin B$_6$, as well as other B-complex vitamins, he found that the patients obtained spectacular relief from extreme nervousness, weakness, excitability, insomnia, and irritability. As proteins work better in concert, the B vitamins prove more effective when taken together in a B-complex supplement, rather than as a single vitamin.

"You know," Fred said, "I'm beginning to get interested in these theories of yours."

"They're not just theories," I said. "They are absolute, proven facts."

"Those antifatigue and antistress vitamins are what I need," he said, "or anything else along that line."

"Calcium is the mineral that keeps your nerves calm," I said. "It enables you to relax from your tensions, and keeps you from becoming unduly grouchy or blowing your top, as you have a habit of doing. Vitamin D helps you absorb calcium, which accounts for the fact that your nerves and disposition improve in the summer when you're outdoors in the sun a lot."

"Come to think of it," he said, "my nerves are better in the summer, especially if I have time to get out and play some golf. But I thought it was just the relaxation."

"That's only a part of it. The leafy green vegetables that you eat in greater abundance during the summer are the best source of another important mineral, magnesium, a component of chlorophyll. According to blood tests, persons suffering from extreme irritability have been found to be deficient in magnesium —and magnesium's digestive helper is vitamin B$_6$. A good vitamin-mineral food supplement will contain both of these food elements, but in the meantime, don't neglect those all-important high-protein meals, eaten three times a day, *regularly.*"

The person getting over an illness or undergoing severe stress should have 100 to 150 grams of protein a day, and children need at least 1 gram of protein for every 2.2 pounds of weight. The normal man or woman in good health, of average weight, and with good digestion and complete food utilization needs 80 to

100 grams of protein a day. But since body chemistry is not the same in any two individuals, and cell nourishment comes only from the food that is digested and assimilated, it is certainly wiser to eat more than the minimum requirements.

Protein is essential for the formation of blood, the restoration of vital tissue and body cells, the healing of wounds, and for the health of your glands.

The only source of this nutrition wonder is from the food you eat each day. And that means plenty of meat, fish, poultry, cheese, seed cereals! Every day!

Your body cells are composed mainly of protein, and when they need renewing and restoring, you can't do it with sweets and starches. Each gram of protein supplies four calories of energy.

If you want to prolong your life, prevent deficiency diseases, avert premature aging, increase your energy and capacity to work, and exterminate whatever personality termites that are undermining your emotional, mental, and physical health, protein can be your most potent ally.

Dr. Norman Jolliffe, director of the Bureau of Nutrition, New York City Department of Health, has this to say about inadequate nutrition: "It is well established that deficiency disease, even without obvious clinical signs, may impair growth, mental development, resistance to many infections, ability to attain the maximum rate of wound healing, and decrease working ability."

Avoid extremes and imbalance. Don't get unduly excited about just *one* vitamin or mineral, no matter how essential it's been proved. Don't forget that they're *all* essential! It's become more and more evident that nutrients are in constant interplay within the body, and every one aids and augments the others.

In your battle against personality termites, each nutrient is needed. Also needed is a variety of good wholesome food, consisting mainly of the high proteins of meat, fish, eggs, poultry, cheese, and the vitamin- and mineral-rich fresh fruits and vegetables, eaten three times a day—plus the midmorning and midafternoon protein pickup, which may be buttermilk, skim milk, a piece of cheese, sunflower seeds, or a few nuts (if there is no weight problem).

Self-pity, anger, unfounded fears, suspicion, self-defeating hate, and other devastating emotions can find no lasting refuge in the healthy body and mind.

Human nature being what it is, they may still enter occasionally, but they'll be outnumbered by the positive emotions of love, faith, friendliness, tolerance, and understanding.

When you feel yourself getting tense, irritable, angry, and almost ready to blow your top, maybe it's time for your protein pickup. After you've established these recommended food habits as a part of your life, you'll soon find your former destructive moods becoming less and less frequent.

Again I quote Dr. Charles Glen King, who, in addition to being executive director of The Nutrition Foundation, is a professor of chemistry at Columbia University:

"It is utterly foolish to emphasize too greatly the role of only one or a few nutrients, such as a *single* vitamin, mineral or protein, or the nutrition of a *single* part of the body ... nutrition scientists are heartily in agreement with us in believing that the only reasonable goal in nutrition is a *lifetime concept of good food habits.*"

14

Is Your Personaltiy Crippled?

HAVE you ever watched the disintegration of a personality? Perhaps you've seen someone you know—maybe even someone you love—a once radiant and promising personality, gradually become fearful, anxious, warped, and literally crippled by real or imagined worries.

You may have longed to help this person. To take him by the hand and say, "Look, things can't be as bad as you think they are. There must be a way out of all your difficulties—let me help you find it!"

It isn't easy to help the crippled personality, but it can be done, if you have enough patience and understanding. He closes his mind and heart to friendly, well-meant gestures, and shuts out those who would be his friends.

He is tense and frustrated from the very moment that he plunges his nerves, his heart, his mind, and his muscles into the driving pressures of the day at that first, nerve-shattering jangle of the alarm clock.

Peace and quiet are not for him, no matter how much he longs for them. He considers his neighbor's TV set a monster, invented by no one less than Frankenstein, and he's ready to commit mayhem at the sound of a baby crying upstairs.

Henry Keane was an example of the crippled personality. His face was tense and worried, he had a nervous twitch in one eye, and his voice was scarcely more than an emasculated whine.

"My life's been a succession of hard knocks," he told me. "I've lost one job after another because of jealousy and ill feeling directed toward me, and I never had a boss who appreciated my work. Right now I'm worried sick because I'm sure that I'm going to be replaced by a younger man."

"I'm sorry things are going against you on your job," I said. "I hope your home life is happy enough to compensate for it."

"*What* home life?" he demanded. "I'm just a meal ticket to my wife and children—and a pretty poor one at that, to hear them tell it. My wife would leave me in a minute, if she had any other place to go. It's a sorry state of affairs when the whole world, including a man's family, turns against him."

I happened to know that Henry had a devoted family, all of whom were greatly concerned over his imagined fears and worries.

His outlook on his family, friends, the world and everyone in it had changed, his work was suffering, and his health was deteriorating. Henry was paying a heavy price for his fears and anxieties. They were crippling his personality.

When you allow worry to gain control of your emotions, it may lead you, as Thomas Mann once said, "one knows not how, to speak of one knows not what," such as Henry's disparaging and unjustified remarks about those who were closest to him. It becomes an anxiety state which won't let you rest. You may forget the original reason for your fears, but the tension is there, and it suffices.

You're caught in a state of fears, preoccupations, or worries that feed upon themselves.

What starts out as fear may become anxiety. Fear is a real threat, but anxiety is an anticipation of a remote threat, that well-known worry over things which never actually happen. If somebody points a gun at you, you're afraid. But you become anxious lest you react in a cowardly manner.

Fear is a high-pitched emotion of immediate danger, an immediate and external threat, usually of short duration, while anxiety is a low-pitched feeling of dread or foreboding which you can live with for years—if you can call it *living*!

Fear and joy are physiologically incompatible. When fear grips you, the emergency system rules, and joy is impossible. Anxiety prevents you from accepting the normal experiences by which you grow and develop to your full potentialities. Both of these emotions contribute to the pathology of a rigid personality structure.

Don't allow fear, worry, and anxiety to remain your companions for any length of time, or they may become habitual. They can cause chronic tension, which is the instigator of many chronic diseases. They can ruin your appetite, shatter your nerves, and wreck your health.

If your fears and worries become neurotic, their influence upon the human body's destruction is immeasurable.

Dr. Grantly Dick Read has this to say about neurotic fear:

> Like an evil propaganda, fear's destructive influence pervades the forces of human life. Were the man in the street to know the truth, its ravages would sound incredible. For my own part, after thirty years of close association with physical and mental derangements of health, I am persuaded, without a shadow of a doubt, that with the exception of unforeseen accidents, the origin of every form of disease, both surgical and medical, whether hereditary or not, can be traced by careful investigation to the influence of fear upon the human mechanism.

Fear cripples the development of personality and stops the learning process.

Unfortunately, the world is full of crippled personalities: unhappy, uneasy, anxious, fearful, half-sick persons whom we call maladjusted.

Gene Tierney, the motion-picture actress, became aware of her maladjustment when her marriage to Oleg Cassini ended after twelve years.

"Just when we were discussing divorce, I began getting sick" was Miss Tierney's explanation. She said that she had always been an idealist, and she was unable to reconcile herself to the fact that her marriage was going to pieces.

"I was heartbroken and filled with hostility and resentment and a million other feelings," she said. "It gradually became too much for me."

After Gene made the motion picture, *The Left Hand of God*, she began suffering from anxiety. She felt extreme fatigue, apprehension, hostility, and tension. The anxiety symptoms grew worse, and the next step for Gene was the sanitarium. There she began to recover from her anxiety state, and learned, slowly and painfully, how to live with herself and her problems.

Worry comes from an Old English word that means "to choke," and it can literally choke your body when it becomes chronic in your life. Dr. George S. Stevenson, medical consultant to the National Association for Mental Health, has this to say about worry:

"Worriers forget that they have the capacity to live through upsetting situations and bounce back when they are over. It's only when emotional upsets come frequently and shake you severely and fail to wear off after a while that there's cause for you to worry."

If you are a chronic worrier, Dr. Stevenson advises you to talk your problems out with some level-headed person you can trust, or to escape for a while into some diversion where you can temporarily lose your problem. Don't be like the French writer who said, "But diversions don't *divert* me!"

You *need* to be diverted occasionally so you can come back and deal with situations when you are more composed. Worry keeps you from ever becoming relaxed. If you go to your job worried, you push yourself and use up a lot of energy, but you accomplish little. And worriers—along with breakfast skippers! —cause 85 per cent of all the accidents in industry.

Worry makes a typist tense her back muscles unnecessarily, and causes her to be more fatigued at the end of the day than the ditchdigger who has used his back muscles with a purpose.

Dr. Walter C. Alvarez of the famous Mayo Clinic has said, "We little realize the number of human diseases that are begun or are accentuated by worry." And according to Dr. Seward Wood, head of the Medical School at the University of Oklahoma, one of his young women patients could turn asthma off and on by turning worry off and on. He also treated a salesman who invariably developed inflammation of the membranes of the nose whenever his mother-in-law came to visit!

The crippled personality can always find something to worry about, from the amount of his social security thirty years from now to the way he'll be able to get along with people of outer space. He refuses to see the many things in his life that are on the credit side, and he concentrates intently on picking up the sour apples instead of the sweet.

If his feelings of worry, anxiety, and fear are not too intense, he may be successful in maintaining outward calm and control, carrying on his normal functions with little noticeable impairment. But such control demands from him extreme preoccupation and meticulousness, and may show itself in a suspiciously exaggerated display of confidence which he's far from feeling.

The presence of these crippling emotions tends to rigidify behavior. Attention moves from the free floating to the concentrated, and spontaneity is lost. Certain features of behavior are exaggerated in a desperate attempt of the personality to maintain control.

A small amount of fear is often a stimulus, challenging the person involved to extend himself. But beyond that, the effects of fear, worry, and anxiety are definitely in the direction of lessened flexibility. The crippled personality has to set up defense mechanisms, for only through them does he feel safe. In some cases this may be caused by a few actual terrifying experiences, but more often it is by chronic situations which he has come to feel are undermining his security.

His troubles increase with the formation of neurotic trends—tendencies that are exaggerated in his effort to maintain security. He steadily builds up for himself a protective organization, but at any point along the way the situation may get out of hand. Anxiety increases and his defenses become more desperate until he finally becomes a full-fledged neurotic personality.

In many cases, of course, this never occurs. Even if a person carries a considerable neurotic burden, he can still work out a way of life that will meet reasonably well his special needs for security and happiness. He can guard against extreme stress or similar traumatic situations which may trigger him over that very thin borderline between the maladjusted individual and the neurotic personality.

Anxiety causes chronic neurotic conflict. The person whose anxiety in human relationships can be held in check only by a neurotic trend of seclusion and withdrawal from society still doesn't obliterate his desire for affection, love, and esteem. These normal wishes needle him from time to time, and cause conflict. He cannot feel satisfied with the limitations imposed upon him by his chief neurotic trend of seclusion. He feels compelled to shut out friendship, companionship, and love, and the mere thought of growing close to another human being sends him scurrying off in the opposite direction.

How can such a person ever be happy? As his anxieties mount, control of his emotions becomes increasingly difficult. His mind begins to be occupied incessantly with his worries, until he can no longer inhibit the bodily signs of fear: restlessness, tremor, perspiration, rapid heartbeat, and quickened breathing. His thinking and judgment deteriorate, and his actions are erratic and poorly controlled. He starts new acts before the old ones are completed, and begins to find it impossible to pull himself together.

Does this sound like somebody you know?

Perhaps, just possibly . . . you?

I hope not. But if you recognize that you are a victim of these emotions that cripple your personality, there are a few things that you can do to help yourself.

In a previous chapter you learned that when your body is poorly nourished your emotions can outweigh your body and mind and gain control of your life. You can begin at once to follow those principles of sound nutrition already advocated, and you can start taking a good vitamin-mineral supplement rich in the B vitamins. (The courage vitamins, remember?)

It isn't too late to train yourself to wear the world like a loose garment, and be relaxed and comfortable in it. Don't allow your feelings of fear and anxiety to weave an emotional strait jacket that binds, constricts, and robs you of freedom.

Oliver Wendell Holmes once said, "There are very few of us who can by-pass the troubles of life. But if you meet trouble as a friend, accept it, and don't worry about it, you'll be better able to handle it."

In brief, learn to accept the inevitable, and realize that what can't be cured should—and often can be—enjoyed!

15

Help for the Inadequate Personality

ALMOST two hundred years ago, in his *Maxims and Reflections*, Goethe wrote: "The botanists have a department of plants which they call *Incompletae*. One may say that there are also *incomplete people*. They are the ones whose longings and strivings are not in proportion with their accomplishments."

At the time of this statement Sigmund Freud, the father of psychiatry, had not been born, but Goethe unerringly described the feelings of frustration which are commonplace talk in our own time. Even Goethe himself felt that he hadn't realized his potentialities and had failed in much for which he had striven.

All of us know one or more of these incomplete people, the inadequate personalities. Often talented, sometimes brilliant, during their youth they usually show great promise. But somehow, somewhere along the way, something happens to them and they fail to live up to those promises.

What holds them back? What handicap keeps them from the success that should be theirs, but always manages to outdistance or elude them?

What are the ingredients of our personality that make up genuine human worth, and how do we determine the qualities that constitute what A. A. Roback, the distinguished professor and author of *Personality in Theory and Practice,* calls the adequacy valence?

The adequate personality has insight (the ability to size up his relation to others and to see himself as others see him, whether he agrees with their opinion or not!); he has sentiment —not to be confused with *sentimentality*—but the sentiment which embraces friendship and loyalty and overflows into sympathy, understanding, compassion, and universal brotherhood.

Perhaps more than any other man of our time, Albert Schweitzer possesses the characteristics that compose the adequacy valence . . . the personality traits of initiative, sentiment, independence, insight, courage, compassion, and energy.

Even now, after a lifetime of work and service for his fellow man, he retains the energy that enables him to lead an amazingly active life under difficult conditions that would discourage an ordinary man. His life may prove to be a legend which will keep our faith in humanity alive for years to come.

Energy may be the key word, I thought, as I looked at an old friend of mine who sat huddled in the chair opposite mine, the picture of a listless, inept, inadequate individual.

What had happened to the Ralph Evans I used to know? The vital, eager, young professor of mathematics who loved his wife, his job, and the world in general? In his spare time he had been writing a book on mathematics made easy, and he already had a publisher interested in the work.

How could he write on *anything* made easy, when the mere task of living appeared to be too much for him?

"I'm not the person you used to know," he said. "I'm all washed up, a complete failure. My marriage has gone on the rocks, my future is insecure, and my health is failing. Tension has a strangle hold on me, and my nerves are shot to pieces."

"Let's take one thing at a time," I said. "First, your marriage. What's the trouble there? I always considered you and Ginny an ideal couple."

"Maybe we were at one time," he said. "But we're not now. I haven't the energy to be a decent husband, and she blames me for not being more affectionate and for always wanting to stay home. The fact is, once I get home I'm absolutely too exhausted to set foot out of the house again. She feels like going out and having some fun, with or without me. But she has nothing to do all day except rest and take a nap whenever she wants to, while I'm under a strain from the time I leave home in the morning until I return at night."

"I was under the impression," I said, "that you liked your job. Why is it such a strain?"

"I love mathematics," he said. "There are no emotions involved in them, and that suits me fine. But I'm a math teacher, and the emotional aspects of teaching are more than I can take sometimes. One of these days I'm afraid I'll grab a fractious student by the nape of the neck and the seat of the pants and shake some sense into him—and that'll be the end of my teaching career!"

No emotions involved in mathematics! Once more here was the neurotic tendency toward seclusion. This inhibitory trend is a direct extension of the defensive process. It occurs most readily when your own impulses have repeatedly got you into trouble (perhaps during childhood), and as a result you learn to consider all impulses and all strong feeling as dangerous. You can impose so many restrictions upon your wants and your emotions that a well-balanced life becomes impossible for you.

"Of course I realize," he went on, "that my nerves are partly to blame, but there's nothing I can do about it."

"Isn't there?" I asked. "Have you ever thought of feeding your nerve cells?"

"Of feeding my *what*?" he asked.

"Your nerve cells," I repeated. "They must be properly fed, if you don't want their depleted energy to contribute to the instability of your emotions. You complained of exhaustion, and often overfatigued persons fail to eat properly. Your nerve cells become depleted through lack of nourishment. They begin to discharge more rapidly and more violently than usual as they pass an impulse on to the next cells. This heightened irritability of the nerve cell discharges makes *you* irritable. You feel tense, jumpy, and all in."

"That's the way I feel, all right," Ralph said, "but I didn't know that my nerve cells were *hungry*. What should I feed them?"

"Vitamin B₁—thiamine—is the vitamin that specifically nourishes the nerve cells. Beef, lamb, liver, heart, or kidney, and whole grains are all rich in thiamine. And vitamin C contributes to the health of the blood vessels in the brain and body and aids in controlling brain fag. But in addition to a vitamin-mineral food supplement containing these and more, you should add to your diet *every day of your life* what Dr. Lester M. Morrison, out of his experiments and vast experience, calls one of the most important nutritional supplements developed in the last fifty years. 'The *least* it can do for you,' he says, 'is to improve your health and give you added vitality. And it may even save your life.'"

"What is it?" Ralph asked. "Is it a medicine?"

"It's called lecithin," I said, "and it isn't a medicine. It's what biochemists call a phosphatide, which is an essential constituent of all living cells, both animal and vegetable. It is a food substance made from defatted soybeans. Lecithin makes up about 17 per cent of your nervous system, and when your body's own supply of lecithin decreases—as you grow older or work under pressure—your nervous system will very likely break down, unless lecithin is added to your diet."

"That sounds exactly like what's happening to me," Ralph said.

As long ago as 1891 Geheimrath Rouleaux, a noted physiologist, found that lecithin plays a tremendously important part in human metabolism, and that it exists in all the cells of the body. It is in the nucleus of all cells, and the nerve and brain cells in particular contain an abundant amount of lecithin.

Many of the nerve fibers are surrounded by a sheath of lecithin (the *myelin sheath*), which nourishes your nerve cells and supplies them with motive force. If they become deficient in lecithin, this fatty sheath is depleted, and the result may be irritability, fatigue, sexual decline, brain fag, nervous exhaustion, or even a complete breakdown.

The nerve cells are rich in lecithin in the morning, but the supply is gradually reduced during the day by nerve strain. Nervous, mental, and glandular overactivity use up lecithin faster than it can be replaced.

Rouleaux discovered that lecithin added to the daily diet was an invaluable aid in improving and maintaining health. It was found to help in overcoming brain fag, nervous exhaustion, headaches, impotence, sterility, and senility.

But at the time that Rouleaux made his discoveries, the only known source from which lecithin could be prepared in any quantity was egg yolk. In fact, the dictionary gives this definition of it: "lecithin, (from Greek *lekithos*, yolk of an egg), a nitrogenous, fatty substance found in nerve tissue, blood, milk, egg yolk, and some vegetables: it is used in medicine, foods, etc."

Even though its beneficial qualities were creating widespread interest among nutritionists and chemists, lecithin was neglected by the medical profession for many years. For one thing, it was too expensive to be used extensively in the human diet, or for large-scale medication. Still more time elapsed before it was found to be one of the constituents of the soybean. Soybean oil contains 2.5 per cent lecithin (egg yolk contains 2 per cent), and at the present time it is obtainable in unlimited and inexpensive quantities.

Lecithin is available in capsule form—a convenience when traveling or working—and in granules, which can be sprinkled on your food or dissolved in juice or other liquids. All health-food stores stock it.

You cannot afford to overlook the vital role that lecithin plays in body chemistry.

During ten years of recent experiments, Dr. Morrison found that lecithin aided in the prevention of heart and blood-vessel diseases, and was more effective in their treatment than any other cholesterol-reducing preparation.

After his years of thorough analysis and many varied experiments, Dr. Morrison is convinced that lecithin is one of our most powerful weapons against an incredible number of diseases, including anemia, rheumatic carditis, diseases of the liver, and kidney disorders. He found unmistakable evidence that it increases immunity against virus diseases, and is valuable in the prevention of hardening of the arteries, since the fats and cholesterol in the bloodstream are dissolved and removed by lecithin.

If that sounds like a large and versatile order for one comparatively little-known concentrated nerve nutrient, Edward R. Hewitt, author of *Lecithin and Health,* gives us the reason for it. He tells us that the main function of lecithin in the human diet is to supply materials which can be converted in the liver into products required by the various kinds of cells in the body.

When lecithin is supplied in the diet in sufficient quantity, it furnishes an amazing amount of the basic materials needed for the proper formation and functioning of the body cells. "It is often for this reason," he says, "that lecithin shows tremendous effects in so many different bodily ailments."

A deficiency of lecithin may well prove to be a nutritional time bomb, set to explode at some later date when you least expect it, into symptoms of nervous disorders, loss of sexual vigor, and a multitude of other deficiency diseases.

Another prominent doctor, N. A. Ferri, has this to say:

> Lecithin has a versatile function in life . . . (It) is an extremely important factor in the digestion and oxidation of fats, thus creating more muscle and glandular activity resulting in greater body exertions and less fat accumulations. Lecithin . . . is essential not only for the tissue integrity of the nervous and glandular system in all living cells but has been regarded as also the most *effective generator and regenerator of great physical, mental and glandular activity. Shattered nerves, depleted brain power, waning activity of vital glands, find in lecithin the most active of all restorers.*

"Dr. Ferri goes on to tell us," I said, "how lecithin affects the various structures of the body. The presence of lecithin, especially in the cellular structure of the nervous system and endocrine glands, *is a source of dynamic energy.* 'The less the amount of lecithin in the diet,' he says, '*the less active are these most vital parts of the human body.*'"

"*All* the parts of my body," Ralph said, "including my brain, are lacking in energy these days."

"Energy is an important part of the adequacy valence of a personality," I said. "And it may mean the difference between success and failure. Haven't you known men with brains and ability who were doomed to failure because they lacked the energy and initiative of men with lesser talents who forged ahead of them?"

"I certainly have," Ralph said, "I'm one of them."

Brains and talent alone are not enough in this competitive age, if indeed they ever were. Independence, initiative, courage, and energy are a few of the qualities that constitute the adequate personality, and these are not found in the person who is half-sick, undernourished, and a victim of one or more of the deficiency diseases.

"I believe wholeheartedly," I said, "that the science of nutrition can help to solve the problems of the inadequate personality. And I'm convinced that lecithin, the most amazing nutritional supplement of our time, added to a well-balanced diet, along with vitamins and minerals, can provide the necessary health, vitality, initiative, and energy needed to combat the inadequacies that might otherwise defeat you."

16

Revealing Traits of Your Personality

HOW do you reveal your personality to others? Are you a perfectionist, a job hater, or an ulcer personality?

If you're a job hater, you may hesitate to admit it. (The boss might be listening!) But the perfectionist is rather smug about his dubious virtue, and the ulcer personality often takes pride in announcing what he considers the reasons for his condition: he's conscientious, hard-working, ambitious, energetic, self-reliant, and successful.

But contrary to what the ulcer personality thinks of himself, his ulcer is *not* the result of overwork. The peptic ulcer almost always is the result of prolonged emotional tension. The victim seems to be trying to compensate in a very characteristic way for some deep-rooted resentment formed in childhood, so he works hard to be successful, strong, and socially acceptable.

However, it is the suppressed conflicts, not the hard work, which causes the ulcer. Peptic ulcers are often a reaction formation in which outward assertiveness and aggressiveness mask a subconscious with very dependent tendencies.

The ulcer personality feels ashamed of these dependencies, so he tries to make himself fit the American masculine pattern, with strong, ambitious, hard-driving tendencies.

But these strenuous efforts are not sufficient to drive his subconscious desires for dependence out of existence, and his body expresses this conflict between active assertion and dependent longings in chronic parasympathetic stimulation of his digestive process.

In a series of eighty cases studied by Dr. G. Draper, it was shown that the peptic ulcer patient is the man (or it may be a woman, although men are much more susceptible to this disease) who has collided in such a way with his environment that he produces a distinctive pattern of personality traits. His outstanding trait is an inner sense of insecurity based on actual or supposed physical inferiority. Of the patients studied by Dr. Draper 84 per cent showed this feeling of inferiority.

The second most outstanding trait of these personalities—regardless of how aggressive or domineering they seemed—was revealed to be a persistent dependence on the mother, or some substitute mother figure, and the fear of losing this person's love and approval. Dr. Draper found this trait in 97.4 per cent of the cases that he studied.

Other traits included jealousy and aggression, which appeared in 64.9 per cent of the patients, and compensatory striving, in 56.2 per cent.

Dr. Draper found that all of his patients were ill-equipped for the competitive struggle which they had mapped out for themselves. Unconsciously these personalities seek the security of a maternal protectorate, yet consciously they must achieve assertiveness with compensatory strivings.

There seems to be no adjustment for the ulcer personality—only constant conflict. Acute attacks may be precipitated by conflict in which the patient feels rejected, thus giving him a sense of failure.

The ulcer personality may suffer from dyspepsia for years before finding himself with an ulcer. Many dyspepsia cases are potential ulcer victims, as there is a close relationship between the two in their emotional disturbances, and a fairly large percentage of the former will develop ulcers if the emotional conflicts become sufficiently severe.

Are you a perfectionist? If you are, no doubt you are proud of the fact—although you have no right to be! As a perfectionist, you are always tense because you must be on guard constantly, for fear somebody will discover your imperfections. You have an egotistical mental image of yourself as a perfect person, and you must avoid at all costs whatever situations might prove that image false. You are so fearful of defeat or failure, and the destruction of your perfection image, that you protect yourself by simply never beginning anything of consequence.

John Hilton was married to a perfectionist. Vera was the type of woman about whom other women said, "Why, my dear, her house is so spick and span that you could eat right off the floor!" When they were first married, John had been proud of Vera's personal neatness, and of the home which she kept so immaculately.

John's office was just across the hall from mine, and as I often work at night, I soon began to notice his light burning late and frequently. One evening about ten o'clock, just as I was finishing up a day's writing stint, John walked in with a thermos in one hand and a sandwich in the other.

"I heard you typing," he said, "and I thought you might like to share my sandwich and coffee. I'm not very hungry, and there's enough for two."

"Thanks a lot," I said, "but I went home for dinner, then came back to do some writing. Did you have to work so late that you couldn't even get away for one of Vera's good dinners?"

"I didn't want to go home," he said. "Vera thinks I'm working late, but I just like to stay down here where I can rest, read, and smoke my pipe in peace."

"Isn't your home more comfortable for resting and reading than the office where you've worked all day?" I asked.

"You'd think it would be," he said. "Anybody would think so, but it isn't. I hate to go home. I'm sick and tired of treating the antique chairs as though they were delicate children. If

I happen to forget and sit down on one, Vera acts as though I've committed a crime. I can't smoke in the house, and I expect any evening that she'll start making me take my shoes off before I walk on her polished floors. Everything connected with the house is *hers*, and although it was my money that bought it, I'm beginning to feel that I have no right there, and that she doesn't want me around cluttering up the place—except when I bring home the pay check!"

Here was a marriage about to go on the rocks. There was no other woman involved, although in time there might be, unless Vera did something about her one hundred per cent neatness which was driving her husband to silent rebellion.

I'm all for rebellion in a situation such as John's, but it shouldn't be silent. If it is at all possible, the perfectionist should be made to realize (before it's too late!) how miserable she can make a man because of her totalitarian desire to have her home—never *their* home, as it should be—exactly the way *she* wants it at all times.

As a perfectionist, Vera was tyrannizing her home and her husband. Other perfectionists, in various walks of life, tyrannize their offices, schools, government—even their own tortured selves. I might be kind and say that Vera is immature; that she's a grown-up child, a spoiled juvenile who has never learned to be a woman and to face reality on an adult basis.

But by probing more deeply into her character, a neurotic trend, found in almost all perfectionists, is revealed.

The self-elevation of perfectionists is the result of either a conscious or a subconscious picture which they hold of themselves. This picture may be an exalted idea of what they are like, according to how they think, feel, and act, or it may be a vague and uneasy awareness that their self-created image is vulnerable.

Vera was unable or unwilling to admit her own shortcomings. She suffered from an inferiority complex for which she must compensate in numerous ways. She explained away her own failings by projecting them onto someone else—by seeing her own faults in others and by criticizing them accordingly. Naturally, her husband bore the brunt of this.

Most perfectionists are suffering from an overworked defensive structure in their personality. There are three criteria by which the defensive overworking can be recognized. First, the perfectionist is *indiscriminate* in assuming a given attitude (not only when appropriate, but even in the most unsuitable circumstances) with the compulsive intensity which doesn't permit it to be adapted to circumstances. Second, such a person is *insatiable*, never possessing enough and never seeming satisfied with anything. And third, when blocked in these insatiable demands, the perfectionist becomes a victim of *disproportionate frustration*, perhaps with signs of anxiety.

The personality traits of the person who is suffering from a compulsive neurosis such as Vera's follow these patterns:

1. There is great interest in orderliness and cleanliness, generally carried to extremes.

2. There is a strong reaction formation to aggressive, destructive, or untidy tendencies.

3. There is stubbornness and stinginess. The compulsive personalities don't want to be hurried or directed, and hate for others to make demands upon them.

4. These victims of the obsessional or compulsive neurosis fear their own spontaneous impulses. Such a basic fear leads to constant effort at control, restraint, and conscious amelioration.

If the compulsives were isolated so that they could do no harm to their families or to society, they wouldn't be a menace. Unfortunately, this authoritarian type of personality is a real menace to democracy, because he doesn't believe in the worth of an individual, but would rather follow a dictator.

As a wife, the rigid, compulsive personality makes life miserable for her family and friends if they don't conform to her standards. She wears herself out with disturbing tensions and chronic, petty dissatisfactions. By her insatiable desire for possessions and her eternal concentration on household perfection, she makes the casual, ordinary affairs of life so laborious that she takes all the joy out of living.

What can you do with such a woman? Was it the perfectionist that Noel Coward had in mind when he wrote, "Some women should be struck regularly, like gongs"?

If you think there's still hope, buy her a copy of the play *Craig's Wife*, and read it aloud to her. Or find a rerun theater showing the old movie, *Harriet Craig*, based on the play, and let her see how another woman drove her husband out of the house and broke up her marriage—all because of her compulsive housekeeping.

The compulsive personalities are so busy keeping up their defense mechanisms that they have no time to grow up and live . . . or love.

Rebel, certainly, if you're the husband of such a woman, but don't do it silently, as John was doing. Rebel loudly, insistently, vociferously, and often, if that's the only way you can show her that it's *your* home as well as hers. And if a man can't spill ashes on his own rugs, where *can* he spill them? Didn't your own easygoing mother used to smile indulgently and say, "It's good for moths," when your father upset an ash tray or dropped his pipe?

"You'll ruin your health," I told John, "by eating sandwiches at your desk when you should be having a good, leisurely dinner at home. And after dinner, I'd suggest that you sit down in one of those precious antique chairs, let go of your tensions, lean back, and relax."

"I wouldn't dare," he said. "The chair would break in a dozen pieces."

"I hope it does," I replied. "Then you can go out and buy yourself a real, man-sized, comfortable chair that you can lounge in and enjoy when you come home tired from the day's work."

"If you keep on encouraging me," John said, a slow grin spreading over his face, "maybe I will. Maybe I'll give Vera the surprise of her life and do exactly that. It looks like some drastic action is needed if I'm ever going to live at peace in my own home!"

What about the job haters? I'm quite willing to concede that some jobs *should* be hated, and if yours is one which doesn't provide an adequate living, an opportunity for your talents, or a chance for advancement, don't go on merely hating it. Do something constructive about it—get another job!

But the job haters who hate *any* kind of job, good, bad, or stupendous, are marked by distinguishing traits. The goldbrickers, the clock-watchers, or the daydreamers who ignore the waiting customer or the ringing office phone are usually immature.

They are incapable of loyalty to anyone except themselves, and will make no personal sacrifice unless they stand to gain by so doing. Dependency is another revealing trait of these immature and fearful job haters. Their parents used to help them with everything, and now they are aggrieved because their superiors, their supervisors, and their co-workers fail to help them in their work the way their parents used to do.

They are unable to assume responsibility. They fail as supervisors because such work becomes for them a nightmare of burdensome detail, intolerable responsibilities, and insoluble problems. They daydream of success instead of working for it, and they maneuver others into carrying their share of the load. They become expert in covering up their failures.

A prominent psychologist, Dr. McMurray, analyzed in depth two hundred and twenty job haters with the foregoing traits, in an effort to determine the cause of their immaturity.

He found that, as a rule, they came from homes where the parents had been overprotective and solicitous. At home the children had rarely had a decision to make. They were spared the hard knocks that build self-discipline and character, and they were denied the opportunity to confront reality or to learn how to live by trial and error.

As a result, they grew up with a sensitivity to criticism. They had not achieved the ability to accept differences of opinion or rejection of their suggestions without resentment.

The job haters should try to develop the three C's of Character, Courage, and Curiosity, according to leaders from fifteen different occupations, who advise: "Start with some native ability, add the ingredients of strong character, intellectual courage, and abiding curiosity, and you just about complete a recipe for success in life."

Undesirable personality traits can be changed, or at least modified to some degree. Dr. William C. Menninger tells us that there are certain important and desirable qualities present in all normal, healthy, mature, and well-adjusted people.

These qualities are real and can be recognized in the people you meet. By knowing what they are, you can look for them and learn to develop them, to a certain extent, in your own personality.

1. *Sincerity:* Complete sincerity is a very rare quality, but when you encounter it you know exactly how you stand with the person who possesses it. There is no sham, hypocrisy, pretense, or phoniness in sincere persons—they are thoroughly genuine.

2. *Personal Integrity:* If you are insincere, it goes without saying that you won't have personal integrity. This trait includes sincerity and the special qualities of honesty, fair play, decency, and loyalty, as well as a deep sense of responsibility and dependability. If you have personal integrity, you are sound; you keep your promises and live up to your obligations.

3. *Humility:* You will find this quality in the really great people of our age or any other, including the Albert Schweitzers and the Albert Einsteins, as well as little-known persons who succeed in combining maturity, strength of character, and

modesty. Humility is never present in the persons who know all the answers before they hear the questions, in the wise guys, the know-it-alls, and the smart alecks.

4. *Courtesy:* So you open the door for your wife and help her on with her coat—even when nobody's looking? Courtesy means more than mere politeness. In its broadest sense it means tolerance, and putting yourself in the other person's place. He's entitled to his opinions, beliefs, and biases, and courtesy means respecting them even if you can't agree with them. Can you, under pressure, in the presence of someone whose major beliefs conflict with your own, remain gracious, considerate, and courteous?

5. *Wisdom:* You may have all of the preceding qualities, but if you lack the wisdom to make use of them, what good will they do you? The wise person has judgment, patience, and the ability to get along with people, because he understands them.

6. *Charity:* This may be the most important attribute for any personality, because in its broadest interpretation it means the capacity to love. We all have weaknesses and faults, but the charitable person looks past them and sees the good in us. To get along well with others requires the charity of forgiveness. Are you big enough and generous enough to be charitable?

Dr. Menninger concludes his list of desirable personality traits with this remark: "Take a good look at yourself for the presence or absence of these qualities. That will help determine how mature you are. And, speaking as a doctor, I can say that maturity is essential if you are to get along with other people and be truly happy and successful."

17

How To Overcome Personality Deficiencies

THE effect of good nutrition upon your personality, like the power of a woman, should never be underestimated.

After changing their eating habits to include high-protein, vitamin, and mineral meals three times a day, I have seen frustrated job haters stop watching the clock, start loving their work—*and* their boss—and even end up marrying him! I've watched those tense, unhappy, and complex creatures, the potential ulcer personalities and the victims of emotional asthmatic attacks, change in a steady, sure, but none the less spectacular way into normal, mature, and likable human beings.

Have you allowed *your* tensions to increase in volume, yet failed to prepare your body with sound health practices and a good diet to cope with them?

If you have, it's small wonder that you hate your job, or that you're beginning to suffer the crippling effects of malnutrition and mistreated emotions.

Tension causes half of all illness. You can destroy your body, mind, and personality with the tension diseases of colitis, migraine, peptic ulcer, arthritis, and hypertension. You can't escape from tension any more than you can escape from life, but you must not allow it to destroy you!

We're using horse-and-buggy emotions and nutritionally robbed diets to cope with cases of jet-age jitters. Our grandfathers ate plenty of fresh meat, whole grains, eggs, unrefined molasses, and leafy green vegetables, thereby providing themselves with an abundance of protein, B vitamins, and other valuable nutrients. They didn't have to worry about atom bombs, nuclear tests, or trips to the moon. It might have been one of them who wrote that old-time verse beginning, "Give me a good digestion, Lord, then give me something to digest!"

They *had* good digestions, and tension diseases were little known in their day. And the effect that a good digestion has on your personality is well stated in Dr. Herbert S. Benjamin's *Your Digestion Shapes Your Life*: "More than just your physical health, that intangible thing called 'you'—your personality, what you put into life and get out of it—is in a large measure determined by the dynamics of your digestive system. From birth on, a large portion of human energy is devoted to getting nourishment and making use of it."

The *quality* of that nourishment is the key to overcoming many personality deficiencies!

We know that tensions set up chemical processes in the body and cause multiple damages which must be repaired with good nutrition and adequate rest. The nerve cells of the brain must be recharged, and the lactic acid must be neutralized in the tired, tensed muscles.

Tension wears you out at an early age.

When you are tense, your body is alerted for an emergency by increasing your blood supply in specific areas. In emergencies, the capillaries in these areas dilate and the blood supply can be increased to eighty times the minimum blood supply needed when you are relaxed or resting. If you freeze or repress your tensions, the hematic segment of your vascular system is slowed down by general vasoconstriction, and the resulting increase in your blood pressure can become troublesome—even dangerous.

Ben Hogan is an example of a man who knew that he couldn't afford tension. (*Nobody* can afford it!) He had to learn to practice his golf shots over and over, mechanically and with *no sense of pressure*. It took several years of this steady, relaxed practice for Hogan to bring his golf swing to its ultimate perfection.

"No sense of pressure!" you say. "I wish you'd tell me just how to avoid it."

You can't avoid it, really. But you can learn to face your tensions and combat them with planned relaxation and a good diet. What you eat can prepare your body to withstand tension, or it can weaken your defenses against it. Diet is of such vital importance in the treatment of tension-caused diseases that it may become a life-and-death matter for the hypertensive personality. Intensive research is now being carried on with formula diets for hypertensives, using skim-milk powder, vitamins, minerals—and lecithin (which contains the fat-dissolving B vitamins, choline and inositol).

Tension can rob you of your confidence, poise, and personality. A beautiful woman, grown tense, loses her looks and becomes drawn and haggard. She may develop irritating, meaningless gestures and fidgets, instead of remaining relaxed and lovely. Age-betraying mannerisms—tight lips, rigid neck and body, and head thrust forward—take the place of her former flexibility, and she is lovely no longer.

"But there's nothing I can do about it," you protest. "Aren't these things just the normal result of aging?"

There *is* something that you can do about it, regardless of your calendar age. *You can eat and overcome personality deficiencies*. You can literally eat and grow younger!

The foods and supplements that keep your body in perfect chemical balance, help you avoid becoming tense and irritable, and aid you in defying the calendar are the cell-renewing proteins, the vitamins, and minerals. The B-complex vitamins are the group that keep your nerves healthy and your tensions under control, and of these, pyridoxine and niacin are the most important. But since all of them are essential, a good vitamin-mineral food supplement is recommended, in addition to three well-balanced, high-protein meals a day.

Vitamins assist you in digesting your protein and in gaining the maximum benefits from it. They also aid in improving the assimilation of minerals. And the minerals known to help you gain relief from tensions are magnesium, which has a quieting effect on the nerves, and calcium and phosphorus, which are essential to normal relaxation and freedom from fatigue.

All of the vitamins and minerals—and protein!—are important vital nutrients, and a serious lack of any of them can and do cause personality deficiencies. The proteins help your body to renew itself, cell by cell. It creates and re-creates itself every second, every minute, every hour. Proteins are also essential to help make the powerful and mysterious substances called enzymes.

The enzymes, in turn, take every mouthful of food that you eat and break it down into the body's nutrients in the process of digestion. The vitamins are the enzymes' helpers, and the minerals assist both in the body's metabolism.

Without protein for the enzymes and without the aid of vitamins and minerals you slow down or stop the process of living in your body and too many of your cells die prematurely.

If, because of an inadequate diet, these cells are not renewed, your body suffers from one or more deficiency diseases. Your brain is more than one-twelfth protein, and it, too, can suffer a chemical imbalance, which might cause a disturbance such as is found in schizophrenia, the most common form of mental illness.

Doctors are now proceeding on the theory that the schizophrenic lacks some vital enzyme which is needed to carry out the biochemical reactions in his body.

Protein starvation reduces production of the enzymes (and vitamin starvation of the coenzymes) which upsets the intricate metabolism not only of the body, but of the brain.

These deranged enzyme systems in the power plant of your brain can produce temporarily deranged personalities.

The symptoms of a disturbed personality are very similar whether the stresses on the brain are emotional or chemical (that is, resulting from absence of dietary essentials). A high-protein diet, fortified with a good vitamin and mineral food supplement, is advised in any case, although the biochemical deficiencies are remedied more easily than the emotional ones.

However, if there are no chemical deficiencies in the body, the emotions are less liable to succumb to stresses in the first place.

Doctors now feel that an abnormal enzyme pattern may be the contributing factor to the reason one personality succumbs to an emotional strain which a sturdier personality tosses off or takes in stride. The time may yet come when science will probe into a disturbed patient's enzymes rather than into his emotional history.

How can you tell if an inadequate diet is affecting your health, your mental well-being, and causing personality disturbances?

Your physical symptoms might be many, including fatigue, weakness, lack of energy, decreased ability to work, dizzy spells, and nervous exhaustion. Your psychic symptoms might be lack of spontaneity, decreased intellective ability, poor judgment, inability to concentrate, irritability, and lack of interest in work, sex, and recreation—leaving little else in which to be interested!

Chemical deficiencies of the body and mind create sick personalities. Correct these nutritional deficiencies with regular meals which include plenty of meat, eggs, fish, poultry, dairy products, fresh fruits, and vegetables, and watch the glowing response of your personality!

Your blood cells can indicate deficiencies, because they are the first to disintegrate when you fail to eat properly. During emotional stress your red corpuscles are forced through constricted blood vessels as they travel through the miles of arteries, arterioles, and capillaries. Ultimately these cells are unable to take any more abuse and die; their fragments are taken up by the liver, spleen, and bone marrow for new blood formation.

Medical scientists have determined that the circulating red blood cells live approximately one hundred and twenty-five days.

It takes good food and excellent health to replace the seven to ten million of these red blood cells that you use up every second.

Suppose you are unable to replace these red blood cells at the same rate that they are used up? Then you suffer a deficiency of them which results in nutritional anemia. Currently, there is a lot of talk about "tired blood"—which is just another name for anemia due to improper nutrition.

When you cannot replace your red blood cells at the same rate at which they are destroyed, there is a departure from good health that often results in drastic personality changes.

Through routine blood examinations, chemical deficiencies and disease tendencies may be pinpointed, and a diet worked out that may help you forestall the onset of disease. If you have inherited a tendency to gout (which is really hyperuricemia, or a high level of uric acid in the blood), the chances are high that you will develop gout if you eat a diet rich in uric-acid-forming substances. But through a routine blood examination this tendency to a high level of uric acid in the blood can be identified, you are forewarned, and by putting yourself on a less rich diet you may escape this disease. By using this same method of identifying your deficiencies or tendencies and using precautionary measures in your diet, many diseases to which you might be subject can be forestalled, checked, or completely avoided.

While some persons are unfortunate enough to be born with faulty metabolism and have difficulty leading a normal life from birth, the majority create their own deficiencies. *The voids created by poor eating habits upset the body's machinery, and real illness and personality disturbances develop.*

The schizophrenic might be born with a chemical imbalance, or so nearly one that a few traumatic experiences might trigger an attack. But you yourself may create the nervous disorders that often characterize pellagra or beriberi by eating an inadequate diet which is deficient in the B vitamins.

An inadequate diet creates chemical deficiencies in the body, and these deficiencies create a sick personality. The sick personality in turn creates neuroses and psychosomatic illnesses.

A few years ago, the late Dr. John A. Schindler, author of *How To Live 365 Days a Year,* gave a talk on psychosomatic illness over the University of Wisconsin's radio station. He said:

> It used to be called psychoneurosis, but now it is known as psychosomatic illness. And it is *not* a disease in which the patient just *thinks* he is sick. The pain is often just as severe as the pain from a gall-bladder colic.
>
> Psychosomatic illness isn't produced by a bacterium, or by a virus, or by a new growth. It is produced by the circumstances of daily living. I have tried to find one word for it, but it takes three, each of them meaning about the same thing, but in different degrees. They are: *cares, difficulties, troubles.* Whenever one has such a thick, impenetrable layer of c.d.t. that he can't get up above it into a realm of joy and pleasure occasionally, he gets a psychosomatic illness.

Cares, difficulties, and troubles seem to decrease when your body is well-fed, your muscles relaxed, and you have the strength to put them to rout. When you are free from hidden hunger you become less tense, and with this easing of tension your nerves find it easier to send messages to that intricate switchboard, your brain, without any short-circuiting due to poor nutrition and tensed muscles. You are able to perform your tasks with less effort, because tension is basically wasted energy.

Ambition returns and you begin to unleash the drive that is latent within you. The job that was a hopeless mass of dull detail and dreary routine becomes a challenge, and it is no longer too much effort just to live.

Purposely, I have avoided the external aspects of personality for two reasons. One is that they have already been discussed at length in articles on charm of manner, miles of smiles, behavior, etiquette, and so on. But the main reason is that I am much concerned about the deeper aspects of personality, and through years of experience I have seen it demonstrated beyond a doubt that if you take care of the inner problems of personality, the outer ones will take care of themselves.

How can you be happy, smiling, gracious, and likable when you're a victim of poor nutrition and the deficiencies of body, mind, and personality that follow in its wake?

Long ago Rousseau wrote, "We are born twice: once to exist, and once to live."

Correct your nutritional deficiencies and your life will truly seem like a rebirth after a dreary, hopeless existence. Perhaps for the first time in many months or years you'll find that you have the energy to stop stagnating and start living—and the inclination to laugh and love again.

With your body strong and healthy, your nerves and emotions under control, your mind alert and optimistic, how can any personality deficiencies defeat you?

They can't, because you'll be well on your way to overcoming them completely!

18

Your Glands: Gateway to Personality

IN HIS excellent book, *Glands, Sex, and Personality,* Dr. Herman H. Rubin says, "You can take it for granted that your thyroid, pituitary, and sex glands have exerted potent influences in shaping your personality. They are closely involved with growth and nutrition; *our personalities grow, too, and need good nourishment.*

"Personality defects are quite conspicuous in marked cases of thyroid and pituitary deficiency, leading to mental sluggishness, lack of spark and animation. Coupled with sex-gland deficiency, the consequence is a personality—or, if you wish, a biochemical oddity—that it is difficult indeed to love."

I thought of this as I looked at Bill Hamilton. His big, football shoulders had wasted away, but he had taken on unusual weight through his thighs and buttocks, his face had grown round and soft, with folds of flesh beneath his eyes and chin, and his open sport shirt revealed a chest without a vestige of hair upon it.

"I had a car wreck," he said. "Other guys come out of accidents like mine with just a few scars to show for it. But look at me!— no broken bones, no scars, but I've grown soft, pudgy—and impotent. What's wrong with me?"

"It's possible that you suffered panglandular shock which has upset your whole endocrine system, and your glands have ceased to function properly," I said.

"How could my glands cause this complete change—and deterioration—in my personality and appearance?" Bill asked.

"There is hardly a single body function that isn't directly or indirectly influenced by your glands," I replied. "They control your nutrition and growth, your sexual activity, your mental development, your appearance and personality. In fact, all of your personality development, physical as well as mental, depends upon the health of your glands."

In his recent book, *The Health of the Mind,* Dr. J. R. Rees, Director of the World Federation for Mental Health, pointed out the control of the glands over the mind. "There are many problems of personality and temperament," he said, "which are almost certainly connected with problems of glandular balance. If we knew what these were and how to remedy them, we should in all probability be able to produce mental changes for which we today labor in vain."

The ductless glands, having no outlet, secrete their hormones directly into the bloodstream and thus affect the nutrition of all your nerve cells. Their influence is complicated by the fact that the secretions of one gland affect several other glands, making it difficult to isolate the functions of any one part of your glandular system. Connected by the bloodstream, the endocrine system works in this pattern: the pituitary gland secretes a particular chemical (a hormone) into the blood and it diffuses through the bloodstream until it reaches the adrenals. The adrenal glands respond by secreting a particular chemical which the blood carries back to the pituitary. This is a signal for the pituitary to slow down production of the adrenals-rousing chemical.

Nice teamwork, isn't it? And in this way the glandular give-and-take maintains a chemical balance in your body.

But suppose your glands become undernourished, starved for protein, or you suffer panglandular shock (usually due to accidents). The disturbances that can develop are many and varied. In Bill's case, it was what is known as Cushing's syndrome, characterized by high blood pressure, weakness, frequent violent headaches, loss of masculinity, round face, and fat deposited grossly around the hips and thighs.

Disturbances of the thyroid gland are generally cases of too little or too much secretion. The thyroid is the metronome that ticks off your tempo of living. When too little thyroid secretion is present at birth, the child is what is called a cretin, or dwarf. As he grows older, his curved spine makes him appear even shorter than his maximum height of three or four feet, and his mentality is equally retarded. His head is too big in proportion to his tiny body; his face is vacuous and devoid of expression.

Studies of 3,548 mentally retarded children in our goiter-belt States of Michigan and Ohio revealed that 281 of them were cretins. Many cases of cretinism have been reported in Switzerland, where there is no iodine in the drinking water.

The adult who is deficient in thyroid secretion (hypothyroidism) becomes dull, lethargic, and coarse-skinned and puffy in appearance. He is so listless and lacking in energy that he is unable to stay awake for more than short periods at a time. He is obliged to nap in his chair, while watching TV, on the bus, and even at work—if he is able to hold a job at all.

Kelp, a natural source of iodine, added to the diet of these dragging, pathetic misfits, has the power to change them into energetic, vigorous, normal personalities once more. Natural sea salt, mixed with 10 per cent kelp, on the table of every home and restaurant in the world would probably eliminate, in time, the possibility of thyroid deficiencies. But since such a large-scale order is not practical, it's up to each individual to see that the salt he uses is *sea salt*—and not the ordinary kind. All health-food stores sell it. And, if he recognizes any thyroid deficiencies in himself, he should keep on hand a supply of kelp tablets—which, unlike drugstore iodine, can be taken freely with no danger—to be used as needed.

An active thyroid has just the opposite effect. The person with a normally active thyroid is quick-thinking, fast-moving, ambitious, and energetic. Perhaps the only difference between the president of a bank and its janitor is merely a few grains of thyroid hormone!

But let the thyroid become *over*active and what happens? Ambition changes to chaotic frenzy and energy to explosive, futile temperament. The overactive thyroid personality (a hyperthyroid) has nervous, spasmodic movements, protruding eyes, a heart that pounds so hard and fast that it is literally racing to its own doom. He may be a victim of *exophthalmic goiter* (not to be confused with simple, colloid goiter, which results from a lack of iodine). More women than men suffer from this condition.

Dr. Rubin lists *poor diet*, overactivity, and a continuous drain of reserves by ruthless self-drive as predisposing factors of this disease. Nervous strain and emotional shocks may also be contributing factors.

The thyroid seems to be the self-appointed shock absorber of your body. By increasing its secretion it makes an all-out effort to make up for emotional shock and psychic injury.

Large amounts of vitamin A taken by the hyperthyroid personality bring about a temporary decrease in thyroid activity. During recent research on radioactive iodine, it was discovered that some foods are also thyroid depressors. The most potent of these proved to be cabbage, rutabaga, and white turnips, with carrots, spinach, peaches, and pears exerting slightly less but still definite influence.

Your pituitary, the master gland, is a pea-sized power house attached by a stalk to the base of your brain. It controls your size, your personality, and your very life. While the thyroid produces only one hormone, the pituitary secretes a number of them. The anterior, or front, lobe of the pituitary produces hormones completely different in chemical effect from those produced by the posterior, or back, lobe of the gland.

The cretin, or thyroid dwarf, has been described. But still another type of minute individual results from an extreme lack of the growth hormone during infancy. The pituitary dwarf is tiny, with a well-proportioned face and body. He doesn't have the oversized head and features, the curved back, and vacant look of the thyroid dwarf. However, as he grows older his child-face soon becomes unduly wrinkled and wizened, like an old man's.

This gland, which exerts control over all the glands of the body, may go to the other extreme. When the anterior pituitary (which controls bone and muscle growth) pours out excessive amounts of the growth hormone, the result is another freak of nature, the giant.

If this happens in an adult whose growth is fully attained, the skull, facial bones, and bony extremities develop disproportionately. This gross enlargement of the extremities, which is called *acromegaly*, was seen in the former Italian boxer, Primo Carnera.

However, the pituitary doesn't always run wild. When it is well-nourished, finely tuned, and in balance with the other endocrine glands, you have a first-rate chance of preserving keen mental powers well into old age. You will be assured of a bone structure that is strong and firm, without a tendency toward brittleness in your later years. Your nerves will remain steady and your sensory faculties acute to the very end of your life.

Your anterior pituitary secretes six known hormones, each with a different function. One is the growth hormone, the occasional disastrous effects of which have just been noted; it also stimulates the growth of hair, skin, and nails. Another, the lactogenic hormone, stimulates the breasts to form milk following pregnancy.

Four hormones stimulate other ductless glands: the thyrotropic hormone stimulates the thyroid, the adrenocorticotropic hormone (ACTH) stimulates the adrenal cortex, and the two gonadotropic hormones stimulate the sex glands.

These chemicals affect the operation of your body and mind with an energizing power that is almost unbelievable.

The potency of adrenalin has been illustrated in this way: it would take 50 miles of water tanks (with 200 tanks to the mile), each one holding 625 gallons of water, to provide water enough to dilute *one ounce* of adrenalin to the point where it would fail to stimulate.

And one ounce of a chemical isolated from the pituitary gland would require 5,000 miles of such water-filled tanks to dilute it enough to render it impotent.

The importance of the chemical aspects of personality have not yet been fully realized.

The chemistry of your body has an undeniable and direct effect upon your personality. You may have seen the sudden and drastic changes of personality caused by certain chemical influences: a deficiency or an excess of thyroid secretion, a bacterial infection, the effects of alcohol or narcotics—all of these can disable a personality temporarily or permanently.

The child, the adolescent, the adult, and the old person each has a different chemical make-up; the glandular source which to a great extent produces the emotional substrata of psychic life accounts for the personality traits at these particular periods of growth and change.

Without relinquishing their reciprocal relation to other parts of your body, each and every one of your bewildering array of cells maintains a chemical process of its own.

If your blood is deficient in calcium and low in phosphorus, it's physically impossible for you to achieve a wholesome per-sonality and a cheerful, optimistic outlook on life.

So, if you find yourself surly, disagreeable, and unable any longer to win friends and influence people, your parathyroids may be to blame for it. It is these glands that govern the calcium and phosphorus content of your blood, and any disturbance in their function upsets the calcium and phosphorus metabolism of your body.

The endocrine gland system is complicated, self-contained, and somewhat dictatorial. But it responds readily to good treatment, to habits, psychic experiences—and to food.

Your emotions can gain control over the chemical reactions of your body through activation of your glands. The glands, in turn, affect your emotions and cause depression or optimism. What you eat can help you avoid these emotional cycles that consist of an over-all upbuilding and giving-out of energy controlled by your glands. By maintaining constant nutrition of your glands through a plentiful supply of proteins, vitamins, and minerals you can control this exhaustion of your surplus energy which causes fatigue, depression, and discouragement, with its consequent loss of personality.

The functional perfection and correlation of your endocrine gland system depend upon your properly balanced protein, vitamin, and mineral food supply. This should include plenty of calcium. Vitamin F helps you utilize that calcium; vitamins B and E and the mineral manganese are of vital importance to the pituitary—your switchboard gland. Iodine and vitamin A are essential for the normal functioning of the thyroid gland in its control of vitality, weight, nervousness, certain skin troubles, and premature aging. Vitamin D is necessary for the parathyroids, which control calcium metabolism. Vitamin B and chlorine help the operation of the thymus gland (sometimes known as the childhood gland).

Without vitamin C and magnesium the adrenal glands cannot operate efficiently, nor can the gonads, or sex glands, function to their capacity without a sufficient amount of vitamin E and the minerals iron and copper.

A nutritional deficiency is almost certain to mean endocrine insufficiency.

Your glands need a plentiful supply of the vital nutrients of protein, vitamins, and minerals every day to manufacture their chemical compounds—the hormones which they send out to regulate the health and activity of your body, mind, and personality.

Your endocrine gland system plays a dominant role in the conversion and utilization of the food you eat. Through the chemical action of your glands, the steak you eat for dinner becomes molecules of body-building protein (amino acids), which can be combined in literally millions of ways to sustain and rebuild the different cells that make up your body.

The islands of Langerhans, scattered throughout the pancreas, control the use of sugar by the body. You can overburden these "islands" of the pancreas with sugars and starches, thus weakening them. When this happens, you are more prone to overweight and diabetes. (The pancreas itself is a digestive gland and not a part of the endocrine system. It produces juices which play a major role in the digestion of proteins and fats. It is the islands of Langerhans which are endocrine glands.)

Your adrenal glands are the regulators of your personality, and you can do them a vast amount of harm by eating superrefined carbohydrates. Proceeding at an emergency pace, your adrenals pour out their hormones and marshal every chemical resource for dealing with the sudden rise in blood sugar caused by sugars and starches. Then comes the drastic drop in blood sugar, and your overworked adrenals are jerked out of balance.

This happens every time you drink a sweet, carbonated beverage, have a cocktail before dinner, put sugar in your coffee, or eat a candy bar or a sweet dessert. In just one day these crises accumulate and put a severe strain on your adrenal glands. Then when they can no longer produce as many hormones as they should, this disturbed function is reflected throughout the endocrine system.

Your body can manufacture sugar (glucose) out of the protein that you eat, and in such a way that the glucose is slowly and steadily absorbed into your bloodstream; your blood sugar level remains constant and your adrenal glands remain calm.

The hormone adrenalin, which is secreted by your adrenal glands, is the emergency compound of your body. It controls your alarm reaction which prepares your body for action whenever danger threatens. It steps up your heart action and causes the pituitary, the thyroid, the parathyroids, and even the sex glands to secrete their hormones to complete the lightninglike preparation your mind and body need in order to deal with

danger. Your lungs enlarge to enable them to take in more air.
Your blood vessels constrict so that the blood is pushed through
them with more force. Adrenalin makes it possible for you to
think quickly, act decisively, and perform superhuman feats of
strength, which would be physically impossible for you under
ordinary circumstances.

"One of the first signs of glandular starvation is sex weakness," I
told Bill. "The contour of your body changes, you lose your
muscular strength and build, the masculine pitch of your voice,
and your stamina. Ordinarily, a weakness in the sex glands shows
up during the male climacteric, but yours may have been brought
on much earlier by your accident."

"Isn't there something I can do," asked Bill, "to restore my
glands, regain my potency, and get myself back to normal again?"

"You can realize that your glands are sick and starved," I said,
"and nourish them accordingly. Feed them enough of the vital
elements of protein, vitamins, and minerals to make up for the
deficiencies from which they are suffering. Sometimes when the
glands have been stimulated by shock, the mechanism for stress
keeps on going, and the glands become damaged by overexertion
or repeated production of hormones."

"Mine were sure stimulated by shock," Bill said, "and I've been
worried and anxious ever since."

"Anxiety is a dangerous form of stress for your glands," I said,
"because the strain on them continues under emotional stress.
In controlling your body through the release of chemicals, your
glands are especially dependent upon the chemicals that you
give them through food. Besides the protein foods of meat, fish,
poultry, cheese, and eggs, you should have lecithin, wheat-germ
oil, and vitamin F, green salads, tomatoes, melons, alfalfa, citrus
fruits, safflower or sunflower seed oil, celery, pineapple juice, and
parsley."

"That's a lot of food to remember," Bill said.

"Yes, it is," I said. "That's why I usually recommend a diet well-
balanced in protein, vitamins, and minerals, with the addition

of a high-quality, potent vitamin-mineral supplement. These enable you to give your glands their vital nutrients without worrying over each item of food that you should eat."

Dr. John Dale Owen of Milwaukee says that a surprisingly high proportion of infertility can be overcome by a balanced diet of protein, vitamins, and minerals. This will restore the body's hormone balance so that the master pituitary gland can send out the needed stimulus to the reproductive system.

A majority of your personality faults can be traced to poor eating habits and the effect this has on your glands. Your good disposition (or lack of one!), your appearance, ambition, energy, initiative, responsiveness, your ability to face life or your tendency to run and hide from it—these attributes and many more depend upon the functioning of your glands.

Feed them well and they will co-operate with you by giving you health of mind and body, sex luster, and a wholesome, radiant personality.

If you deny your glands their daily vital requirements, death can begin for you at forty. But you can invest in glandular health and reach the age of sixty or more physically fit and sexually proud. Your glands are indeed the gateway to personality—at any age!

19

Eat Your Way to Magnetism

MAGNETISM is a magic quality that can open doors to love, friendship, success, and personal accomplishments.

Its possessor doesn't need the magic words of "open sesame" to unlock those doors for him. Nor does he need pull or influential friends—he can influence *anybody!*

"I'd like to have the quality that can do that for me," you say. "What can I do to achieve it?"

Your can literally eat your way to magnetism!

Now, wait a minute, you fatties, with the greedy looks on your faces! This definitely doesn't mean that you can gorge yourself on what you mistakenly regard as goodies—the sugars, fats, and starches that are available in vast quantities in pies, cakes, and other pastries. Nor does it mean overeating. Those are two sure ways to extinguish whatever flicker of magnetism you already have.

This is a statement that will bear repeating: *you can, not calorically, but scientifically, eat your way to magnetism!*

"I don't see how I could ever have magnetism," you say. "Just look at me! No, on second thought, you'd better not—I'm not much to look at. I haven't any personality, and I'm a real homely guy."

What gave you the idea that the possessor of magnetism has

to be handsome? He doesn't. In fact, some of the most handsome men and women are absolutely devoid of it.

Offhand, try to think of a few magnetic personalities of today. Who comes to mind? Certainly not the current crop of handsome Hollywood lads striving to become the Clark Gables, Gary Coopers, and Spencer Tracys of tomorrow.

But Gable, Tracy, and Cooper themselves, all far from being handsome in the accepted sense, bear the authentic stamp of magnetism that lasts through the years. It is the vibrant, enduring quality which has nothing to do with perfection of face and figure, but which has a great deal to do with the health, enthusiasm, and vitality that come from excellent nutrition.

"Sure," you say, "but they're actors. It's part of their business and training to develop magnetism. What about us ordinary guys?"

Ordinary guys? When you eat your way to magnetism, you cease to be an ordinary guy. You automatically lift yourself out of the ordinary category and into the exceptional one.

But if you want examples in other walks of life, there are many of them.

One of the most powerful and magnetic personalities of our time is Winston Churchill. Brilliant, dynamic, compelling, and persuasive—but did anybody ever call him handsome? And has it ever mattered in the least that he is less than Adonislike in appearance?

The beloved Albert Schweitzer, perhaps our greatest living personality, possesses magnetism of a high degree. To live the courageous, energetic life to which he is dedicated requires health, stamina, and endurance. If he had neglected his own health, his nutrition and dietary needs, the loss to humanity would have been great. An ill, undernourished, or maladjusted man would never have the energy to achieve the miracles for mankind that Albert Schweitzer has been able to accomplish.

Let's go back into the past and consider some of the devastating women of history. Cleopatra, the siren of the Nile, for whom Marc

Antony threw a world away, is reported to have had an ugly nose and a poor complexion. But Cleopatra did all right in spite of them—with sheer personality and magnetism!

King James II brushed off some of England's greatest beauties for a baffling series of homely (but magnetic!) women. Here is Lord Macaulay's pen portrait of King James's last love, Catharine Sedley: "Personal charm she had none, with the exception of two brilliant eyes, the lustre of which, to men of delicate taste, seemed fierce and unfeminine. Her form was lean, her countenance haggard."

Professor R. E. Baber made extensive studies of the standards that American college men use in choosing a wife. He found that almost all of them rated a good disposition, magnetism, and a pleasing personality above physical attractiveness.

Professor Baber's conclusion was this: "Beauty is such an elusive, indefinable attribute that it need not depend upon regularity of features and conformity to an accepted type, but is determined partly by the reflection of personality through face and body, revealing such factors as animation, kindness, courage, and grace."

And T. F. James, in *The Truth About Falling in Love*, says: "Contrary to the opinion of our fiction writers, intelligent Americans attach far more importance to personality traits than to physical appearance."

Some imperfections of face and body are often considered desirable to remind us that a woman is warmly human, magnetic, and alive. "If a woman is perfect, she will go through life like a statue—untouched" is a famous photographer's observation.

All this talk about magnetism and what it will do for you, but just what is this magic, intangible quality?

You know what a magnet is, of course, and what its function is. It draws things to it. And according to the dictionary, magnetism is "the power to attract; personal charm or allure." It even further defines it as mesmerism.

But whether it's mesmerism or magic, the magnetic personality does attract others, with no apparent effort. I prefer to think of this quality as innate vitality, which some are born with and others must work to achieve.

So you think you weren't born with it? All right, then, let's get to work on it!

"I have so little pep that I can barely drag myself around" is a common complaint. "How can I achieve magnetism when my family and friends consider me a neurotic, a sympathy seeker— and sometimes just a plain nuisance? They don't understand that I simply don't have the strength to keep up with them and their activities. What can I do about it?"

First of all, you can get that whine out of your voice and stop feeling sorry for yourself. Stop moaning about your exhaustion to your family (maybe you *are* doing it partly to get attention) and start eating with a purpose.

Harvard University's Department of Nutrition states: *"Nutrition is the most important single environmental factor affecting one's health and vitality."*

What did you have for breakfast? If it was nothing more than a sweet roll and coffee, you don't deserve any sympathy.

Your breakfast should be a meal which contributes all the protective nutrients that prevent deficiency diseases. It should raise your blood-sugar level and keep you from feeling tired, sluggish, listless, and generally cantankerous.

If you want to get your body's machinery going in high gear, first eat an orange or half a grapefruit. For variety you might sometimes have melon, berries, or other fruit rich in vitamin C. Then have eggs and meat, and perhaps a cooked whole-grain cereal. (Millet is especially good.)

Winston Churchill was mentioned earlier as an exponent of magnetism, and his capacity for work and pleasure, his amazing endurance and vitality are the envy of men half his age. A typical Churchill breakfast includes half a cold partridge, eggs, and tea. Apparently a protein-for-every-meal man (which explains his inexhaustible vitality), his evening meal nearly always consists of an outsized roast with plenty of vegetables. His wife has said of him, "A good dinner is essential to his health and happiness."

Don't get the mistaken idea that you can eat your way to magnetism simply by consuming lots of calories. It's the *type* of calories you eat that does the trick. You can stuff yourself constantly with carbohydrates and still be pepless, joyless, loveless, and friendless, with no more magnetism than a blimp—which you may come to resemble closely if you're not careful.

Protein is the food that a pallid personality needs. Give a little time and thought to the care and feeding of *your* personality and see how quickly it responds to good treatment.

All right. Let's assume that you're off to a fine start with a nourishing breakfast. With lunch and dinner still to go, don't be a backslider. Make every meal equally nutritious, varied, and appetizing, built around a main dish of protein food—meat, eggs, poultry, fish, cheese. Whenever possible, have both a yellow and a leafy green vegetable, and a green or raw vegetable salad.

Dessert? Why, certainly! Anything you like—as long as it's some kind of fresh or frozen fruit (canned is all right if it's water-packed and not in heavy syrup), melon, berries, or cheese. Occasionally you might prefer a stewed dried-fruit compote of apricots, prunes, pears, or peaches, cooked with a bit of lemon or orange rind and sweetened with honey instead of sugar.

If you think you absolutely can't *live* without a piece of pie once in a while, be sure it's made with a *single* graham-cracker crust—and a fresh fruit filling only. Then if you have enough will power, you'll be better off to eat the filling and leave the crust!

That's a stern schedule, you think? Not at all! You'll be surprised at the way you'll lose your desire for sweets on a high-protein, vitamin, and mineral diet. A craving for candy and rich desserts often indicates hidden hunger, low blood sugar, and other nutritional deficiencies. Correct these deficiencies with an adequate diet and notice how soon you'll cease to drool over chocolate layer cake and whipped cream pies.

You don't have to take my word for it. Try it and see for yourself.

Fatigue is the archenemy of magnetism. If you don't eat enough protein, enzymes cannot be formed in adequate quantities to produce the energy you need. If you eat meat only once a day, and seldom touch eggs or cheese, you probably are not getting sufficient protein to create good health, vitality, or magnetism.

"But proteins are expensive," you say. "I can't afford to have them for every meal."

You can't afford *not* to have them! If money is no object, you can buy the finest New York cut sirloin steaks, but the inexpensive ground round steak is just as good a source of protein. A sweet roll will cost you ten or fifteen cents, while one egg, at current prices per dozen, will cost only a nickel. Six of the most concentrated and least expensive proteins which can be added to your diet in a variety of ways are powdered skim milk, nonfat cottage cheese, brewers' yeast, wheat germ, millet, and sunflower seeds.

Without protein your personality may all but perish—and unfortunately so may you!

If you want to be a lovely, lithe, and young-looking grandmother, you might take Mrs. Arthur Murray as a model. Well over fifty, Mrs. Murray exudes magnetism and fairly bubbles with animation. She and her husband have a strenuous schedule to maintain, and know the value of keeping physically fit. Long ago they realized the importance of eating for health and energy.

"We always start the day with a hearty breakfast," she says. And for other meals they enjoy a variety of well-balanced food which gives them a feeling of well-being. "Whatever makes the juices run" is the way she puts it.

Watching the Murrays' beautiful muscular co-ordination on TV, I am more than ever convinced that both their training and superior nutrition are responsible for it.

A lack of vitamin B_{12}, in particular, seems to be one of the major causes of poor muscular co-ordination and downright clumsiness.

You might remember this when your teen-ager (who quietly and desperately longs for magnetism) is going through the awkward stage of falling over his own feet and not knowing what to do with his hands.

Rapid growth increases his vitamin requirements, and a B_{12} deficiency may partly account for his embarrassing habit of stumbling, fumbling, and knocking over everything within reach. B-complex vitamins and high-protein meals can help him through this difficult stage and aid him in attaining the confidence and poise for which he is struggling.

Have you ever wondered why one person, with little to be gay about, can remain lighthearted and sparkling, while another, with everything in the world to make him happy, is completely miserable?

If there were only one thing standing between you and your sought-for magnetism, it could very easily be a niacin deficiency. This B vitamin, niacin (or niacinamide), isn't obtained as easily from your food as some of the other vitamins are. Kidneys and fish are a good source of it—but how often do you eat them? Yeast, wheat germ, and liver contain some, but these, too, are foods that you don't go around munching constantly. Nuts and eggs are a fair-to-middling source, so it's a fairly safe bet that you aren't bursting at the seams with niacin!

Pellagra (at one time called *mother's disease* because when food was scarce it was the mother who denied herself and suffered the deficiency so that her children might eat) results mainly from a lack of niacin.

While the B vitamins have often been called the courage vitamins, niacin has been specifically dubbed the morale vitamin. If you have a niacin deficiency, you may expect anything from a moderate to an appalling change in your personality. The most optimistic and courageous person can change into a cringing, fearful, worried, suspicious, and extremely depressed individual. His capacity for enjoyment diminishes to the vanishing point, and he often feels that life isn't worth living.

When niacin-rich brewer's yeast is added to such a person's diet, the response is fast and effective. For many years, brewer's yeast has aided in the recovery of pellagra patients. Your own body can manufacture niacin if you provide it abundantly with protein and B vitamins, but, as stated before, the B vitamins work better in concert, as their action is synergetic, or mutually re-enforcing. An oversupply of one B vitamin may cause an under-supply of another—which is another reason why I advocate the *balanced* diet, with the addition of a good vitamin-mineral food supplement.

In choosing a vitamin-mineral food supplement, make sure it is as complete as possible. The more complete the formula, the more you get for your money—and the better vitamin-mineral insur-ance you have. I have found that for my own use the splendid formula called Nutri-Time is an ideal vitamin-mineral food sup-plement. It contains over seventy different vitamins, minerals, and other nutrients. You might want to look into it for your own use. It is available in most health-food stores.

Nutrition is even an important factor in the way you kiss. No, I am *not* letting my imagination run away with me. It's a matter of record, based on good authority.

Dr. Carlton Fredericks explained the relationship between nu-trition and kissing on a radio broadcast over station WOR.

"When a fellow kisses a girl," Dr. Fredericks said, "the adreno-sympathetic system calls on the liver for glycogen for energy. This in turn forces the release of insulin, vitamin B_1, and phos-phorus to burn the sugar. In his brain, if he is doing any thinking (which is problematical), there is an exchange of starch, phos-phorus, and thiamine between the thalmic and the cortical brain.

"As the pulse and respiration rates rise, there is increased exchange of oxygen on the intracellular level, which would mean increased consumption of thiamine and phosphorus."

There you have the opinion of one expert. So if you want to excel in the art of kissing, make certain that you're well-nourished and fortified with proteins, vitamins, and minerals.

To sum it up, eat your way to magnetism—and never be caught with your glycogen down!

20

Three R's for Adults

YOU learned your childhood readin', 'ritin', and 'rithmetic years ago, but there's always some new threshold of knowledge to enter.

"Not for me," you may say. "It's a little late for that. After all, I'm getting older, and it's difficult for an older person to learn anything new."

You think so, do you? Well, here's what our foremost authority in the study of aging, Dr. Edward J. Stieglitz, says:

> The false concept that you can't teach an old dog new tricks has done a great deal of harm. First of all, it *is* false, and secondly, it is a wonderful alibi for indolence . . . Let us take, for an example, the rate of learning. I choose rate of learning because speed is an attribute of youth. As measured by a group at Columbia University, the rate of learning reaches its peak at the age of 22. At the age of 80 it is about the same as at 12.
>
> A 12 year old can learn extremely fast—but so can an 80 year old if he's interested and wants to learn. As you grow older, your memory may slow down a little, but it tends to become more accurate.

Professor Carl Camp of the University of Michigan carried out an experiment to compare the memory of young men and older men. He took two groups of university professors, one group 35 to 40 years of age, the other group 65 to 75. He had them

190

memorize a nonsense paragraph from the *Congressional Record* and recite it back to him. The older men took slightly longer to memorize the paragraph, but their score of accuracy was considerably higher. Each one said almost the same thing, "I wanted to be sure, so I went over it again a couple of times." Actually, they may have learned it just as rapidly as the younger group, but they took a little more time to insure accuracy.

You can learn at any age if you're interested enough, if you believe you can, and if you really try.

And by a not-so-strange coincidence, I have something right here that you can practice on. *Three R's for adults*—easy to read, not difficult to memorize, and good advice to follow.

1. Recharge your life.
2. Renew your body and mind.
3. Revitalize your personality.

After retiring from her glamorous career in motion pictures, Gloria Swanson recharged her life, renewed her body and mind, and revitalized her personality—which didn't even need it!

She now has three children and six grandchildren, and in the interest of her family's health, she became a serious student of nutrition. After a thorough study, she is convinced that the processed foods (the packaged cakes and sweet rolls with synthetically colored filling, the TV dinners with preservatives added to keep them fresh indefinitely, the refined sugars and starches, and many more) that are sold with such ballyhoo and served on millions of tables are responsible for the deterioration of mind and body in both children and adults. She also believes that the effects of such foods are to blame for a horrifying percentage of juvenile delinquency.

She goes on to say that it's frustrating to know that most of the public are gullible enough to think that our pure food laws protect us from eating anything that would harm us.

"Nothing could be farther from the truth!" she says.

On juvenile delinquency, she says, "The crimes committed

without passion or motive by juvenile delinquents, for the sheer thrill of it, must be conceived and committed by sick minds . . . Much has been written on the matter of mental ills and nutrition. Since the average person now accepts the fact that rickets, pellagra, scurvy and many other physical ills are being eliminated by proper nutrition, why can't they accept the fact that the mind might be made healthy by healthful nutrition?"

At an age when many women are content to remain passive and indolent, Miss Swanson has enthusiastically and vigorously recharged her life. She did it with new, intense, and varied interests: a career in designing, her study of nutrition, and her growing concern with juvenile delinquency and its problems.

"But I have no special talents as she has," you say. "I'm not a career woman, and I couldn't make a speech if my life depended on it. I don't know about all these things that she discusses so easily. I've never had many interests outside of my home and family."

If your husband, children, and home are your main interests, we don't need to look any farther. There are enough new things to learn in those three departments to keep your life recharged and your mind renewed for a lifetime.

If you're an average mother with two or three children, it's more than likely that one child is different from the others. Perhaps he has emotional problems that his brothers and sisters have never experienced. What do you do about it? Do you put his moods down to temperament or tantrums, or do you try to find out the underlying cause of his trouble?

Is he more frail in physique and a less hearty eater than the other children? Do you often have to threaten, coax, or bribe him to eat? Do you wonder why he dawdles, while the other, sturdier children clean up their plates and ask for second helpings? What's wrong with him, anyway?

What *is* wrong with him? Isn't it worth your time and trouble to find out and correct it? Don't put the blame on heredity and toss it off with, "Oh, my mother was always a very finicky eater, and he takes after her. He's moody and nervous, too, the way she was."

It's much too easy and far from accurate to explain away a child's disturbances, his lack of appetite, and emotional upsets in this manner. Look more deeply into the underlying causes, and you may be able to prevent future juvenile delinquency and mental illness in such a child. If he fails to eat nutritious meals he undoubtedly is not getting sufficient protein, vitamins, and minerals to maintain health in mind and body.

The University of Southern California in their famous reprint, *Is Mental Illness Mental?*, says this:

> The following is the range of mental disorders *induced by insufficient intake of vitamins:* lack of thiamine results in ideas of persecution, mental confusion, and loss of memory; lack of riboflavin causes depression, visual disturbances, disorderly thinking, inability to concentrate or perform mental work, and forgetfulness; lack of niacin means depression, anxiety, irritation, loss of memory, mania, hallucinations, and dementia.

If your child is deficient in any one of the above B vitamins, it may result in failure in school, confusion, and depression. A deficiency in all of them could cause seemingly insurmountable problems which might result in juvenile delinquency or mental illness.

Isn't the study of a subject which could decide your child's future health and happiness well worth your interest and enthusiasm?

According to Dr. Herbert Pollack, consultant on food and nutrition to the Surgeon General, United States Army, *you can increase your child's life span by as much as 10 per cent, or about seven years, through proper feeding.*

Dr. Pollack, who is also a member of the Food and Nutrition Board of the National Research Council, goes on to say:

> These same principles of choosing foods with proteins, vitamins, and minerals in proper proportion to calories offer you and

your husband the possibility of living more healthily and longer.

When you reach middle age, or if you are in that category now, you and your husband can enjoy greater stamina and better working efficiency. When you are in your sixties or seventies, or if you are there now, you may stave off degenerative diseases; if you already suffer from any, you may slow down their development.

Why not put this on your list of new interests to recharge your life: planning stay-young-and-healthy menus for your entire family, every day, for the rest of your life?—which is certain to be longer and happier if you follow such a program!

A few added years of happy, healthy life for you, your husband, and children, are indeed a priceless gift. By now you know that you and every member of your family must have a daily balance of protein, vitamins, and minerals—foods which enable your bodies to draw from them the atoms and molecules needed for fuel, growth, and bodily repair.

Because of faulty body chemistry which prevents complete utilization of food, some persons need more vitamins than others. And since even in the best diets much of the vitamin content is lost in the cooking, handling, or storage of food, I strongly advise a good vitamin-mineral food supplement in addition to three well-balanced meals a day.

A drama was enacted that made history a few years ago in Dr. Tom Spies' nutrition clinic. Into this clinic, from the Birmingham, Alabama, area, came 893 prematurely aged and feeble invalids. Most of them had been given up by doctors, even though laboratory tests had ruled out the possibility of any standard chronic diseases among them.

What was wrong with these pitiful wrecks, some of them no more than thirty, yet already old and broken in body, mind, and morale? They complained of aches, pains, and exhaustion; they suffered from various nervous, digestive, and mental ailments. Most of them had been unable to work for years, and there seemed to be no hope for them.

Then, almost miraculously, hope *did* appear on the horizon, and one by one their symptoms began to fade. Pain, weakness, and despair were replaced by new strength and vigor. What was the secret?

The nutritionists had been put to a mighty test, and had won!

These patients, labeled hopeless cases by their doctors, were all suffering from nutritional failure, due to multiple vitamin deficiencies. In an all-out-for-total-recovery effort, the Birmingham researchers fed these desperately sick people diets rich in proteins, vitamins, and minerals, added dried brewer's yeast and liver extract to supply them with other needed chemicals, and gave them massive doses of vitamins and minerals.

The impossible task was completed. All of the 893 invalids were rehabilitated, and went back to their various jobs.

According to Dr. Paul de Kruif, this experiment encouraged many practicing physicians, and proved that premature aging can be reversed and the prime of life prolonged.

And the man behind this and many subsequent triumphant experiments in nutrition, Dr. Tom Spies, tells us: "The expensive way to use vitamins is to avoid them, develop nutritional failure, lose your health and your job."

Dr. Spies has proved that supercharging your well-balanced diet with a potent vitamin-mineral supplement will give you the resistance to combat disease, fight off infections, and forestall premature aging.

He has also reported his success in the treatment of hundreds of undernourished and prematurely aged children. (That's right! Even children age prematurely when they are deprived of proper nourishment and adequate vitamins.) By adding large quantities of powdered skim milk—rich in protein, calcium, and B vitamins—to the children's diet, the premature aging process was reversed, and they soon became normal, healthy specimens of carefree childhood once more.

Have you noticed that more and more children seem to be wearing glasses than they did some years ago? If so, you noticed correctly. The rate of nearsighted children has been increasing with each generation.

But a heartening discovery by Dr. F. A. Gardiner, who has been studying this problem of the young for some time, may bring about startling changes.

If the child's nearsightedness is due to a refractive error (which frequently appears in the growing eyeballs of young children), diet will correct it, he tells us. A diet in which the total calories are *at least* 10 per cent animal protein has been proved effective in his experiments with several hundred nearsighted children.

"A nutritional problem was exposed in these nearsighted children," he said, in his report to the British medical journal, *The Lancet*.

When the nearsighted child is fed a diet deficient in the complete animal proteins, this refractive error becomes worse, and the child may end up with very little sight.

In Dr. Gardiner's experiments, deterioration slowed down in the sight of those children who were given 10 per cent of their daily food requirements in the form of meat, eggs, and dairy products. In a year's test, vision improved in many of these children, some of whom were already over twelve years old.

The various ways in which you can improve the health, happiness, and well-being of your husband, your children, and yourself provide an endless and fascinating subject for you as a homemaker.

In discovering and applying these principles of nutrition, you won't need to look any farther for means of renewing your body and mind.

But what about revitalizing your personality? Don't give it a second thought! Your personality, that outer reflection of your inner self, will respond to the methods used in renewing your body and mind. Automatically, almost magically, it will revitalize itself.

Dullness will change to enthusiasm, and drabness to sparkle.

Take a good, long look at yourself.

Can't you see the beginning of it now?

21

How To Make People Like You

THE bumblebee is unable to fly.

Laboratory tests, wind tunnel experiments, and the theory of aerodynamics prove that he can't. The size, weight, and shape of his body in relation to his total wingspread make it absolutely impossible for him to fly.

But the bumblebee doesn't know all this—so he goes right ahead and flies, anyway. If he knew anything about aerodynamics, he might lose confidence in his soaring wings and forever after be obliged to crawl through life.

But he believes in himself and flies, regardless of the odds against him!

The way you act when the odds are against you may very well be the final deciding factor in whether or not people like you.

Are you a whiner when things go wrong? Do you put the blame on somebody else, and never admit that it might have been your own fault? Do you go on a rampage and make everybody else miserable when you don't get your own way? Are you convinced that fate conspires against you, and do you consider the world a dismal, frustrating place filled with people who are untrustworthy, ungrateful, and unfriendly?

Nobody likes a whiner, a pessimist, or a chronic complainer. If you're a whiner, you wouldn't even like yourself if you could see your faults as others see them. Your friends—if you have any left!

—may put your irritable, faultfinding ways down to temperament or just plain cussedness.

It could be. But your symptoms also could be those of a vitamin B deficiency, or a lack of calcium, or the starvation of your glands by a prolonged protein, vitamin, and mineral deficiency.

Your glands are the regulators of your personality, and in case you've forgotten, the B vitamins are the courage and morale builders. A serious lack of them can change a courageous, friendly optimist into a chronic grouch who is suspicious, pessimistic, and hostile.

Perhaps you have the grace to be ashamed of your nuisance value to yourself and others, and underneath that ornery exterior lies a longing to be liked. You don't want to be an injustice collector who never forgets the slightest, most unintentional hurt, and who makes a production out of every real or fancied affront. You'd like to be gallant in the face of misfortune instead of whining about it, and you need help in overcoming fears, hostilities, and confused thinking.

The vital foods that can change pessimism into optimism, the fears of the inadequate personality into courage, and the slow, befuddled thinking of the constitutionally inferior into clear, quick thinking are the B-complex vitamins, glutamic acid, and minerals.

The likable personality and the healthy, efficient brain are the reflections of a well-nourished body. At no time in life is your brain a finished product, because your blood is continually nourishing it.

You never outgrow your need for calcium, one of the most vital minerals in your body. Tense nerves and a grouchy disposition are among the first signs of a calcium deficiency.

Scientists have discovered that each cell in the central nervous system has a sheath of some calcium compound just within the outer wall. Whenever the integrity of this sheath is impaired through a lack of calcium, the cell becomes excessively irritable. There is no longer the insulation against the spread of the electrical impulse, and you fail to channel your nerve impulses properly. So, rather than a focused response, you receive a bunch of irritations.

That's rather like being on a perpetual party line, with your phone ringing every time there's a call for anyone on the line, and that can make anyone grouchy!

The gradual demineralization of your body is part of the process of growing old. Without enough calcium, your bones become thin, brittle, and easily broken. If you're still in your middle years, you can prevent this demineralization by deliberately increasing your intake of foods rich in calcium and other minerals before the process of aging actually starts. Dry skim milk is an ideal way to get your calcium, because it's low in fat but high in protein and important minerals, as well as the nerve-soothing B vitamins.

Dr. Henry C. Sherman of Columbia University found that *only two patients out of four thousand* that he examined in a New York hospital had an adequate calcium reserve in their bodies.

In a good vitamin-mineral supplement you get all the necessary minerals for your body's optimum health, such as magnesium for your skin, digestion, and nerves; zinc for your thyroid gland, pancreas, and sex organs, and manganese for your brain and nerves.

Minerals help vitamins in their work, just as vitamins assist your digestive enzymes. Cobalt is the helper of vitamin B_{12} in the building of the hemoglobin of your blood; magnesium works in concert with vitamin B_6 as a preventive and treatment for nervousness, insomnia, mild or severe tremors, convulsions, and palsy; and potassium works with vitamin E in maintaining a normal pace of the heartbeat.

When you feel like retiring from the human race and your family and friends almost wish that you would, you can be sure that your body is deficient in something that is stopping its chemical processes. Unfortunately, the mineral deficiencies don't show up in your body until it's almost too late—your marriage is on the rocks, your disposition gone to pot, your job in the balance, and you are aging prematurely or suffering from some chronic disease.

The majority of persons are fairly vitamin-conscious nowadays, but the mineral story is still too little known.

Without minerals, your personality can run down like an old, worn-out clock. And a *grandfather* clock, at that!

There's another extreme type who is equally as unpopular as the grouch, the pessimist, or the complainer. He's the arrogant, inconsiderate show-off who needs toning down. The life-of-the-party lad or lass who must always be the center of attraction and can't bear to share the spotlight with anybody else; the joker whose wit is barbed and aimed primarily to hurt or humiliate someone.

If you are this type, then according to an eminent psychiatrist, Dr. Martin Grotjahn of the University of Southern California, you're sick, sick, sick!

The German-born, German-educated doctor has made a study of the cause and meaning of laughter and its relationship to the unconscious. He's written a book on the subject called *Beyond Laughter.*

"A wit is an angry man in search of a victim," Dr. Grotjahn says. "A witticism is his way of releasing repressed hostilities. If he doesn't find a victim, he will probably suffer from a migraine headache attack."

A witticism starts with an aggressive tendency, or the intent to insult or shock. By camouflaging the insult with laughter, the wit makes it acceptable to society, and in this way releases his own bottled-up hostilities.

After a thorough study of both amateur and professional comedians, Dr. Grotjahn arrived at these conclusions:

The kidder: This one expresses his own conflict with authority (usually his parents) by imitating the father torturing his "kid."

The caricaturist: He insults people by deflating and humiliating them, with a stroke of his brush or his pen, in a sophisticated and supposedly amusing fashion.

The clown: He represents the depreciated father figure, once strong and all-powerful, but now reduced by ridicule to a bumbling, inept, ludicrous figure of a man.

"But laughter," Dr. Grotjahn adds, "as it provides a permissable release of unconscious aggressions, is one of the best safeguards of mental health. In fact, the comedian is a friend of psychiatry, even though he himself is sick and doesn't know it."

The business of having a likable personality resolves itself into being agreeable instead of disagreeable, gracious instead of rude, friendly instead of aloof, responsive, cheerful, and possessed of an easy, outgoing confidence and naturalness of manner.

Two of the factors which are important in determining how well you're liked are (1) the attitudes you show toward others, often without realizing what you're revealing about yourself; (2) the methods you use in trying to handle people.

Stanley C. Allyn, a newspaper boy who worked his way through school and became president of the National Cash Register Company, says, "Today the most useful man or woman in the world is the man or woman who knows how to get along with other people. Human relations is the most important science in the broad curriculum of living."

Mr. Allyn himself is a likable, pleasant man who is generous with his praise whenever possible. He believes that the key to good human relations in business, as elsewhere, is in helping people to help themselves.

Never fumble an opportunity to be friendly to any human being.

Perhaps no man has ever been more popular with everyone, in all walks of life, than the late Will Rogers. Here, in his own words, is the reason for it: "I never met a man I didn't like."

The beloved Mary Martin, like the bumblebee, is unable to fly. But she believed in herself and did it—when she played Peter Pan in the theater and on television—flying from Never-Never Land into the hearts of millions of people.

Not young, never a beauty in the conventional sense, Mary Martin is one of the most successful and universally loved stars of all time. What's her secret of making people like her?

Mary, who walks (or flies!) out on a stage and glows with love for her audience, has a creed that she's lived by since childhood: to be a friend to all.

She's never too busy or too tired to go out of her way to help others. Joshua Logan, her director, says, "Next to my family, I love Mary more than anyone else in the world." And her husband puts it this way, "Unlike most stars, Mary is a dream to live with."

If Mary ever had occasion to go to an endocrinologist, I'm sure that he'd find her glands well-nourished and in excellent working order. They'd have to be to produce a disposition as wonderful as hers. And where do her vitality and boundless energy come from? Her love of life and everybody in it!

When asked about the "secret of her endless bounce," Mary Martin had this to say: "Diet is very important. I eliminate carbohydrates and concentrate on protein, fruit, green salads, and vegetables." Which is another way of saying that Mary lives according to the principles laid down in this book.

In the intricate arrangement of your protein molecule, which is nature's masterpiece of complexity, is locked the secret of life. The proteins are the materials and the builders of life: they fashion its tissues, regulate its energy, and assure its continuation.

But your body has to change the protein you eat into the material necessary to build new cells. This is done through a series of chemical processes which are called *metabolic processes.*

Each of these incredibly complex and sensitive series of metabolic processes must be sparked by vitamins and minerals. Without them, the process is stopped, and stress, fatigue, virus, or bacteria can attack the tissues of your body. The delicate balance of your physical personality becomes upset.

And, like a fine bridge, your physical personality is only as good as its weakest point.

Under stress, your body's machinery shows a rapid wear and tear. Severe strain or an emotional upheaval are a shock to your body's processes, and if care isn't taken, your emotions can start your body on a chemical derangement which results ultimately in personality deterioration.

First comes a loss of self-criticism and judgment. Attention and concentration then begin to show impairment, and the speed and accuracy of mental work decline. Motor and sensory performances resist somewhat longer, and unless your nervous system is given proper nourishment and relaxation, you lose such skills as handwriting, and finally experience definite impairment in your visual and auditory perception.

Naturally you don't experience all of these symptoms suddenly. You may merely find yourself becoming irritable and hard to get along with, or suffering a feeling of depression and experiencing difficulty in concentrating on your mental tasks.

Your feelings of depression and inadequacy occur most often on an empty stomach, and tests have shown that food relieves tension. Dr. Gerald Brill, a New York City Health Department physician who is in charge of one of New York's nutrition clinics, says, "When you are under tension, *don't skip a meal.* Stomach acids increase when a person is perturbed. This may result in increased tension. Food is the best neutralizer of this stomach acid."

A New York restaurant, frequented by advertising executives from "ulcer row," features a daily "executive tension luncheon." On this luncheon you may find consommé, sliced tenderloin of beef, and other high-protein, nonirritating foods which should be eaten by persons under stress.

As long ago as 1825, a French connoisseur of food, Brillat-Savarin, wrote in *The Physiology of Taste*: "Digestion is of all bodily functions the one which most affects the moral state of the individual. The manner in which it is habitually performed makes us sad, gay, taciturn, talkative, morose, or melancholy, and we do not suspect the cause."

To be a likable personality, you must meet and vanquish conflicts, blocks or frustrations, infantilism, and defeatism. You must get rid of your blind spots of prejudice, unthinking dislikes, stubborn views, nostalgia, and fear of new things.

If you refuse to grow up, look for escapes instead of facing facts, harbor the envy, hate, and worry that go along with mis-evaluation and defeatism, you aren't likely to win any friends or influence *anybody*.

Two disagreeable aging personality types are the arbitrary or tyrant, and the querulous or complaining. I'd like to take these personalities while they're still young, put them on a high-protein, vitamin, and mineral diet, with an added supplement rich in B complex, and watch them stay young longer and grow old gracefully!

If they were particularly weary, depressed, and intolerably can-tankerous, I'd give them a cocktail three times a day before meals. A pep cocktail, made of two teaspoonfuls of type 200 brewer's yeast, one teaspoonful of desiccated liver powder, and one table-spoonful of lecithin granules, mixed in a glass of tomato juice.

No one can fail to benefit from the invigorating and energy-producing effects of such a cocktail. It may be just the boost that a tired, colorless personality needs.

We advance to wisdom through progressive stages of ignorance. The healthy personality doesn't make himself miserable by dwelling on unpleasant possibilities—or even on *pleasant impos-sibilities*. He accepts what he has and makes the most of it.

Put out of your mind the things that can't be attained, and de-vote your energy to what *is* attainable.

Health in mind and body are within your reach, and so is a likable personality. But you won't achieve them just by reading this book, or any other. You have to apply what you've learned, and make it work for *you* as it has for countless others.

If it were in my power to do so, I would organize every man, woman, and child in a crusade against protein, vitamin, and mineral deficiency. Armed with the weapons of sound nutritional knowledge, we would stamp out this evil in our midst, this national malnutrition that weakens the personality, body, and mind of so many people.

If you have eyes to read, ears to listen, and willing hearts and hands, you, too, may help in a cause as urgent as the cancer, heart, and multiple sclerosis drives.

In correcting deficiencies caused by poor nutrition, we aid in the prevention or help in the cure of many dread and unnecessary diseases.

What can *you* do?

You can tell your family, friends, and acquaintances of these nutritional principles that we have explored together. You can apply them in your own life and invite others to emulate your example. Best of all, you can teach your children, so that they and their children may grow up with more vital personalities, keener minds, and stronger bodies to live in a happier, healthier world than we have known.

Will you join me in this crusade?

Index